LIFE NATURE LIBRARY

THE LAND AND WILDLIFE OF

SOUTH AMERICA

TIME
LIFE
BOOKS
®

LIFE WORLD LIBRARY

LIFE NATURE LIBRARY

TIME READING PROGRAM

THE LIFE HISTORY OF THE UNITED STATES

LIFE SCIENCE LIBRARY

GREAT AGES OF MAN

TIME-LIFE LIBRARY OF ART

TIME-LIFE LIBRARY OF AMERICA

FOODS OF THE WORLD

THIS FABULOUS CENTURY

LIFE LIBRARY OF PHOTOGRAPHY

THE TIME-LIFE ENCYCLOPEDIA OF GARDENING

THE AMERICAN WILDERNESS

FAMILY LIBRARY

    THE TIME-LIFE BOOK OF FAMILY FINANCE

    THE TIME-LIFE FAMILY LEGAL GUIDE

LIFE NATURE LIBRARY

THE LAND AND WILDLIFE OF

SOUTH
AMERICA

by Marston Bates
and the Editors of
TIME-LIFE BOOKS

TIME-LIFE BOOKS   NEW YORK

About the Author

Marston Bates is a man with two vocations: he is a full-time writer and a full-time naturalist. "I don't know whether there is, or should be, any difference," says Dr. Bates, who was in high school when he published his first scholarly work, *A Geometrid Larva on Grapefruit*. During his undergraduate days at the University of Florida, he wrote reams of short stories and poetry; in return he received reams of rejection slips "from all the best known magazines."

Pursuing his childhood ambition to visit the tropics, he went in 1928 to Central America, where he became deeply engrossed in tropical fauna and flora. His zeal attracted the attention of the Director of Harvard's Museum of Comparative Zoology; he was granted a fellowship and went on to receive his Ph.D. in 1934. Since then Dr. Bates has collected butterflies and moths in the Caribbean, studied malarial mosquitoes in Albania and conducted research in human ecology on a coral atoll in the South Pacific. For eight years during and after World War II, he headed the Rockefeller Foundation's yellow fever laboratory in Colombia. He is now an internationally known authority on tropical America.

A member of the National Science Foundation, the American Academy of Arts and Sciences, and many other scientific societies, Dr. Bates is now professor of zoology at the University of Michigan. He is the author of nine definitive works in various fields of natural science. Among those dealing with South America are *Where Winter Never Comes* and *The Forest and the Sea*. His first—and now classic—book, *The Natural History of Mosquitoes*, was written during his years in Colombia. He is married and has four children.

ON THE COVER: A keel-billed toucan prepares to feast on a cluster of palm fruit. Toucans usually travel in groups, marauding other birds' nests and shattering the calm of the forest with their raucous screams.

Contents

The text for this book was written by Marston Bates, the picture essays by the editorial staff. The following individuals and departments of Time Inc. were helpful in producing the book: LIFE staff photographers Alfred Eisenstaedt, Eliot Elisofon, Fritz Goro, Yale Joel, Robert W. Kelley and Dmitri Kessel; Editorial Production, Norman Airey, Nicholas Costino Jr.; Library, Peter Draz; Picture Collection, Doris O'Neil; Photographic Laboratory, George Karas; TIME-LIFE News Service, Murray J. Gart.

Introduction

THE South American continent stretches from the tropical Caribbean to storm-swept Cape Horn. Small, as continents go, it is a little more than half the size of Africa, and a third the size of Eurasia. Yet it contains within its borders the greatest continuous tropical rain forest in the world, the largest river and longest continuous mountain chain. Along its western coast lie stretches of true desert. It boasts all kinds of open country; the vast grasslands of the pampas grade northward into the savannas of the Chaco and southward into the wind-swept plains of Patagonia. Temperate rain forests flourish in the shadow of the southern Andes. So great a diversity in climate and topography has long offered innumerable opportunities for the evolutionary radiation of plants and animals. Thus, it is not surprising that the South American fauna and flora are among the richest in the world, and in some ways the most peculiar.

Many of South America's plant and animal groups are not known or are poorly represented in other continents, and this becomes the more marked as we go back in time. Our knowledge of the geological history of South America is now sufficiently good to permit the statement that no direct connection with any other continent existed for about 70 million years until the Isthmus of Panama was completed only two or three million years ago. Prior to the rise of the Isthmus the descendants of those animals and plants that at various times had managed to reach South America had evolved in isolation. The peculiar forms of today—the sloths, anteaters, armadillos, monkeys, various rodents and marsupials—are the descendants of pre-Isthmian ancestors; the more familiar ones—tapirs, deer, raccoons and cats—came down from the north via Panama. The story is one of the most fascinating in all the long history of life.

Man was a latecomer to the Americas. The ancestors of the American Indians arrived in time to see only the last survivors of some of the great groups of mammals that had flourished in earlier days. The human story in South America is a fascinating, colorful and often violent one. This volume is not concerned with it, however, but instead emphasizes the land and its features, and the animals and plants in all their wonderful variety.

The editors of this handsome book are fortunate in their author. Anything written by Marston Bates is a delight, and Bates on a theme with the scope of this one—well, the reader may judge for himself.

BRYAN PATTERSON
Museum of Comparative Zoology,
Harvard University

1

A World Apart

For many years my wife and I lived in a small town in eastern Colombia, at the base of the Andes where these greatest of South America's mountains give way abruptly to the great plains, the llanos, of the Orinoco River basin. The fascination of the place never dimmed. Near the town, there still existed fragments of forest that had never been cleared, and primeval conditions persisted within a few miles of the newly made roads. Behind us the mountains towered, climbing thousands of feet past dripping cloud forests to alpine heights. In front of us, to the east, the band of forest along the mountains' edge gave way gradually to open savannas and finally to the grassy plains that stretched with scarcely a break to the horizon. South of us, the forest extended ever farther out, a hundred miles and more to where the streams flowed not into the Orinoco but into the Amazon. We were on the margin of the greatest untamed, unexplored wilderness in the world.

We had a whole range of tropical landscapes within easy reach of our town— only desert and seashore were lacking. This was fascinating enough in itself, but beyond this there was, ever present, the thrill of possible encounter with the unknown. For despite the schoolbook familiarity which many Americans may feel for this sister continent, South America is very much a land of mystery and surprises, and this applies as much to the scientist as to the tourist seeing it for the first time.

For one thing, this was for uncounted eons an island continent, cut off from the rest of the world until a land bridge was established to the north between two and three million years ago. Thus its inhabitants followed quite separate evolutionary developments until they were invaded from the north, and what exists today is a unique mixture of the old life and the new, offering a subject of study as rich as it is promising. The larger animals of South America, for example, have by now almost all been collected, described and given scientific names, but this is only the beginning. Of their habits, how they live, reproduce and exploit their environments, in many cases little or nothing is known. Some of the smaller animals there have seldom if ever been seen at all, and when it comes to the inconspicuous but omnipresent insects, most kinds have not even been collected and named.

TAKEN as a whole, the fauna of South America is the most distinctive of any of the continents. Only Australia is comparable, but there the animal life is much less rich and diverse because of the smaller size and less varied living conditions of that largely arid land. South America, by contrast, offers every type of land and climate from the driest deserts to the wettest rain forests and highest mountains, with enormous areas still as virgin as when the first Portuguese and Spanish explorers planted their countries' flags there four and a half centuries ago.

How many people realize, for example, that the great Amazon-Orinoco river basin, a tremendous wilderness as large in area as the United States, is still, in practical effect, an inland sea? Yet this is so: its land is slowly rising now, and what was for almost 400 million years a salt-water environment has gradually turned into a fresh-water river system. This has led to some unusual adaptations of oceanic creatures to a fresh-water existence. Alexander Humboldt saw fresh-water dolphins swimming among the trees when the upper Orinoco, hundreds of miles from the sea, was in flood in 1799, and manatees gurgle there, fresh-water cousins of the "sea cows" normally found far to the

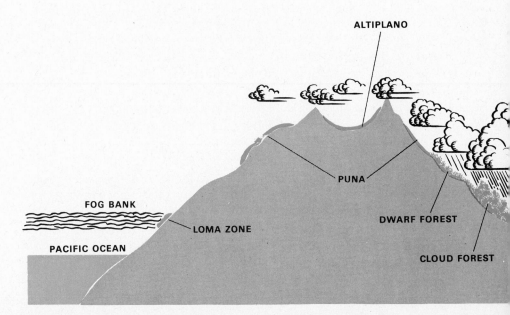

east along the Atlantic coast. There are skates and rays in the rivers, a giant river otter six to seven feet long, and also the world's biggest rodent, the capybara. Here, where rivers are in flood for almost half the year, even some rats have webbed feet so that they can swim. A baffling creature is the only known water-adapted marsupial, a water opossum—how do the young fare in the pouch when it swims?

Because they cannot survive in this watery wilderness, many animals of the Amazon and Orinoco basins have either taken on aquatic adaptations or taken to the trees. There are more prehensile tails here than anywhere else in the world —monkeys have them, and opossums, and porcupines and kinkajous. There is a tremendous variety of species, many of which have still to differentiate completely into their respective niches: they defy classification and lead to endless arguments among taxonomists. A single acre of forest crowded with trees might contain so many different species that scarcely two of the same kind would be found, and much the same might be said on a larger scale of mammals and birds. The rodents and bats of South America have more varieties than on any other continent, and there are more than twice as many endemic families of birds as in Australasia or Africa.

This is the vast heartland of the Neotropical Realm, on whose fringes we lived—the largest and most continuous tropical forest left on this earth and the least disturbed by any human activity. Behind us lay an area no less fascinating: the mountains which, not dwarfed by any foothills, rose almost straight out of the jungles. In a few miles, the road to Bogotá coiled up to 5,000 feet and there, where the clouds drifted in from the plains, began the "weeping woods" of local lore, the cloud forest of the ecologists. In the damp air, the trees were loaded with mosses, orchids, ferns and other epiphytes. The air turned ever cooler as the road climbed upward, and the soil clung in an ever thinner mantle to the underlying rock. As growing conditions became increasingly difficult, the vegetation became more dwarfed and sparse, until finally, at 10,000 feet, the twisted trees and shrubs and the lichen-covered boulders formed the kind of miniature landscape that is aptly called "elfin woodland." Above the tree line lay the puna, bleak and cold as the tundra of the far north, and above this, the perpetual snow of the great peaks.

HOW THE ANDES MAKE WEATHER

This cross section of the Peruvian Andes shows the effect the high mountains have on weather in South America. Warm, damp trade winds from the Atlantic rise up the eastern slopes and become progressively cooler. This causes the moisture in them to condense and fall as rain, heaviest in the area of the cloud forest. Higher up, the rains get lighter and lighter, and there is first a dwarf forest, then the grass of the cold puna and finally the permanent snow of the peaks. Between the snowy eastern and western ridges lies the altiplano, an agricultural area subject to seasonal rains.

Weather conditions are completely different on the arid western side of the Andes. There the warm ocean winds become chilled and form a fog bank as they pass over the icy Humboldt Current which upwells along the coast. Blowing ashore, the fog settles in the loma zone on the slopes, where the moisture in the air is enough to support seasonal vegetation in what is otherwise a plantless desert.

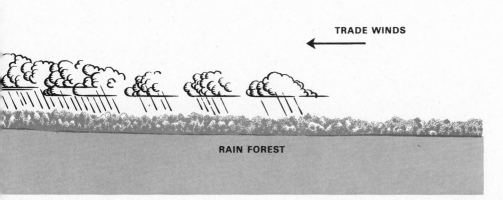

TRADE WINDS

RAIN FOREST

The mountains of South America have played as important a part in the development of the continent's plants and animals as have the lowlands. Some, like the Andes on the west coast, are comparatively new as we measure geological time; others, like the Guiana Highlands on the northeastern Atlantic coast, are very old. To the invaders from the north which came across the land bridge, the mountains provided a highland route along which many of them could penetrate to the farthest reaches of the southern lands.

The northern invaders included, of course, a great many animals of the same Neotropical environment as the South American heartland; of these we shall hear more later. But among them, too, were species accustomed to cooler, drier climates, and in the southern continent these took the mountain roads. Thus we find bears close to the equator but high above the steaming jungles. There are shrews in the highlands of Colombia and Ecuador. Mountain lions range from British Columbia all the way south to the Strait of Magellan—one of the greatest ranges of any mammal species known. Weasels came down the cool mountain avenues, as well as some small cats and skunks. One weasel type called the grison was tamed by Indians and trained to hunt out the native chinchillas for their fur, much as Europeans train ferrets to hunt rabbits and rodents.

CHINCHILLAS, the mouselike creatures with the beautiful, soft fur, are among the endemic species of the mountain areas, as are the members of the camel family—the guanacos and vicuñas of the high Andean deserts and plains. A burrowing rodent known as the tuco-tuco is the equivalent of the American pocket gopher in the high plains, and there are plant species in the mountain habitats, some evolved there, some brought down by walking or winged invaders, many of which have not even yet been named.

The Andes form the backbone of the continent. This is one of the world's great mountain systems—not as high as the Himalayas (Mt. Aconcagua, at 22,834 feet, is still considerably short of Everest's 29,028) but erecting, for nearly 5,000 miles along the Pacific coast to the southernmost tip of Chile, a wall that reaches high into the region of perpetual snow. The high plateaus and mountain lakes, the upland forests and cloud-draped wooded valleys and the long extension from midtropics to the cool south temperate zone provide more varied conditions for life than any other mountain system in the world. One reason for this diversity lies in its compression of life zones: any mountain range of any consequence offers successive layers of differing habitats from the foothills to the peaks, but in the Andes, rising so steeply to such altitudes, these life zones are crowded very closely on top of each other and, since many of the high peaks lie in the equatorial region, the vertical range of climates is extreme.

Along the Pacific coast of northern Chile, for example, lies the Atacama Desert, one of the driest strips of land on earth. In some parts of this 600-mile stretch of seared, brown earth, rain scarcely ever falls; most parts know a shower only every 10 years or so. Yet straight up from this arid land the mountains rise, life zone atop life zone, right up to an Arctic climate, then to fall away again on the eastern side. Less steep on this face, the peaks give way to the high plateaus where the guanaco and vicuña live, and the domesticated llama. Farther south along the eastern base of the Argentine Andes is another type of desert, which, spotted with drought-resistant shrubs and cacti, is reminiscent of Arizona. And here, too, are found ecological equivalents of Arizona's desert areas—burrowing cavies like pocket mice, which plug their holes by day, armadillos and a saguarolike cactus.

A CLIMBING PALM

Among the climbing plants of the Neotropics is the jacitára, "the terrible," which looks like a vine but is actually a palm. It gets its nickname from the thorns occurring along its entire length. These are most formidable at the tips of the long switches, where they harden into curved hooks. As the jacitára grows, its sprawling, free-swinging switches brush against other plants and the hooks grab hold. Supported in this way, the jacitára often becomes 60 to 70 feet long.

To the east and south, as the traveler flies after crossing the Andes, lie the pampas, one of the world's great grassland regions. Here the American westerner has a familiar feeling: he might be flying from Denver to Chicago. As far as the eye can see is the rolling, grass-covered plain that fades out gradually into semiarid Patagonia, which in turn gives way to the bleakness of Tierra del Fuego. Yet, if they are superficially reminiscent of America's great plains, the pampas have notable differences in their animal life.

Unlike North America, the pampas have had no large grazing herds of native hoofed animals in the last million years, though man has in his own time made them one of the great cattle countries of the world. There were deer, but the cattle and hunting have crowded them out. Today there are small herds of guanaco; there are foxes, skunks, vizcachas—an ecological equivalent of North America's prairie dog—and the Patagonian cavy, an equivalent of the jack rabbit or hare. And there are rheas, the big, flightless birds so reminiscent of the ostriches of Africa and Australasia's emus and cassowaries.

To the biologist this rich and varied continent is the showcase of the Neotropical Realm, which extends north from the continent itself over the narrow Isthmus of Panama into Mexico. The line between the Neotropical and the Nearctic to the north, which includes the United States and Canada, is impossible to draw with geographical accuracy, since plants and animals of the border regions tend to mingle. This book, then, may on occasion range as far north as central Mexico, but for the most part its concern will be the heartland of the Neotropical, the South American continent.

How long, and why, was South America isolated from the rest of the world? That is impossible to say, since the earliest history of the world's southern continents is a matter of scientific argument—whether, for example, some continents at one time abutted each other and then drifted apart, or whether there existed at some time an Antarctic continent, Gondwanaland, of which South America was once a part. But we do know that at least from the early Paleocene to the late Pliocene, a period of some 60 million years, South America was an island, and during this period most of its distinctive animals evolved.

THE history of the continent can most surely be deduced from the fossil record of the mammals. The history of birds, of other vertebrates and insects can for the most part only be guessed at from the evidence of living forms, since the fossil record here is very incomplete. The mammals, however, give us a glimpse of how the fauna developed during the long period of Tertiary isolation and of what happened when land connections were again established with the major land masses to the north. Before this happened, these creatures were able to develop undisturbed in a world apart—and insular South America produced some very curious mammals indeed.

Back in the early Paleocene, when South America was an island, mammals everywhere were for the most part small, unspecialized creatures. The Age of Reptiles had just passed; the mammals were barely on the threshold of their great period of growth. But it is likely that by this time they already had developed two distinct types, distinguished by their reproductive processes: the placentals, which developed their young internally in the womb, nourishing them through a connection to the mother's blood supply until they were advanced enough to come forth into the world, and the marsupials, which bore their young when they were little more than embryos and nourished them externally, most often in a pouch of the mother's belly, but sometimes only half-hidden by her fur, in whose protective warmth they clung to her teats until they could survive on their own.

Placentals and marsupials had varying success in the various parts of the world. In Australia it was chiefly the marsupials which became established and dominant. In the world continent, on the other hand, only the placentals survived. But in South America both marsupials and placentals developed side by side during the time of isolation, evolving into numerous and diverse forms. And though many of both types became extinct when the re-establishment of the land bridge brought in the invading creatures of the north, South America today shares with Australia the distinction of having the only marsupials still thriving in any numbers.

Thus there are today 14 genera of marsupials in tropical America (by contrast with 64 in Australia and its outlying islands), occupying a wide variety of habitats and niches. It is difficult to say just how many species there are, because South America is still so largely unexplored that the record is incomplete. Even some of the "species" that have been named might be only subspecies. As a hypothetical example, a type of yellow, mouselike opossum living on the east coast of Brazil might seem to be quite distinct from another mouselike opossum living in the Andean foothills of Bolivia; yet because between the two lies such a vast and trackless terra incognita, no one can say what intermediate types linking the two might not still be found.

The range of possibilities permits fascinating speculation. During the continent's long insularity marsupials were to be found in many ecological niches now occupied by placentals. Fossils show a wide variety, ranging in size from mouselike species to animals the size of bears and lions. Judging from their tooth structure, they also must have had a wide variety of habits: some of them had teeth adapted for gnawing, like rodents; some seem to have been insectivorous; and some undoubtedly ate almost anything they could find and digest, as our opossums do today. But the most remarkable of these ancient marsupials were the carnivores.

ALL the known meat-eating mammals during the period of South America's isolation were marsupials. Most of these are classed together in a family named the Borhyaenidae, and many of them were hyena- or wolf-like, with rather short legs, strong, compressed claws and large skulls. One of them, named *Thylacosmilus*, had large stabbing canines, remarkably like those of the completely unrelated saber-toothed tiger.

These marsupial carnivores all disappeared before the end of the Pliocene. It seems clear that the placental carnivores that had been evolving on the world continent—members of the cat family, the dog family and the weasel family—had become more efficient in many ways, and when they were able to enter the continent across Panama, the marsupial carnivores could not withstand the competition. Only the smaller and less specialized marsupials survived the late Pliocene invasion of new mammal types, and so it is their descendants which populate the continent today.

The placental mammals of South America's time of isolation were just as curious as the early marsupials. Five distinct orders of hoofed mammals, for example, roamed the continent, each very different from the other in basic structure and different from any of the living orders of mammals. Even the names of the orders are unfamiliar to most of us: Condylarthra, Litopterna, Notoungulata, Astrapotheria, Pyrotheria.

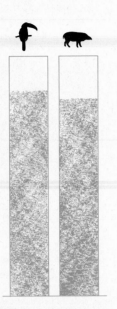

A RESERVOIR OF UNIQUE BIRD AND MAMMAL FORMS

Sixty million years of evolution in isolation from other continents has produced among South American birds and mammals a very high percentage of species that are found nowhere else. As shown by the colored section of the left-hand graph, about 85 per cent of all the birds known to inhabit South America are endemic forms. The remaining 15 per cent are either winter migrants, sea birds or other types also known to live in other places. For mammals the figure is only slightly lower: 82 per cent are endemic.

Some of these hoofed mammals of the past must have looked like animals of today, although they were quite unrelated; others, judging from the bones, were extremely odd. Some looked like rhinos, hippos, camels and elephants; among the litopterns, some developed horselike hooves back in the early Miocene, 10 to 12 million years before horses themselves reached a comparable stage of development. On the other hand, another litoptern, known as *Macrauchenia*, was built like a modern llama but had a snout vaguely like that of a tapir, a creature certainly different in appearance—and quite likely also in habits—from anything we know today.

In addition to marsupials and these five extinct orders of ungulates, an order of mammals which we now know as Edentata developed—a few in North America, but the great majority of them in South America. Some of the edentates are still with us: the armadillos, the sloths and the anteaters. Most of them are now extinct in both continents.

Today we divide the edentates into the armored types—the armadillos—and the hairy types—the sloths and anteaters. These two separated very far back in geological history. The ancient armadillos were not too different from their living relatives—like them, their armor was composed of plates, or scutes, separated by flexible bands. But long ago the armadillos had a curious group of relatives, now extinct, known as the glyptodonts, which were quite different.

In the glyptodonts the armor was a solid shield, a carapace, like that of a turtle. Some of them had heavily spiked tails, like war clubs. At the peak of their development, they seem to have been very large, eight or nine feet long, and with their high, domed shells they must have been a formidable sight. Florentino Ameghino, the Argentine paleontologist, concluded from evidence such as bones and human artifacts found beneath glyptodont shells that early men might have used these big carapaces as ready-made shelters.

There was greater diversity among the ancient hairy edentates, the forerunners of the modern sloths and anteaters. Today we know only two genera of sloths, one with two toes on its forefeet and the other with three (both have three toes on their hind feet), and both of these inhabitants of the rain forest are tree-dwelling animals which move about in the deliberate manner that gave them their English name. The sloths of ancient times, by contrast, all seem to have been ground-dwelling animals. Most of them grew very large, about the size of the average modern bear, but there was at least one widespread type which was enormous—its skeleton reached a length of 20 feet, which made this creature, known as *Megatherium*, larger than an elephant.

Since the Panama land bridge was a two-way street, some of the ancient edentates and other mammals also moved north, so that for a time, sloths and glyptodonts lived in what is now the southern United States. Why they became extinct there we do not know; it could not have been so simple a matter as predation by creatures like the big cats, for the southern immigrants survived for several millions of years. Yet eventually, during the Pleistocene, they did all disappear, along with many mammals from the world continent—mammoths, mastodons and various species of the horse family that once roamed the North and South American plains.

It is clear, however, that the ground sloths, like the glyptodonts, were still around when man began to populate the New World. Ground-sloth remains have been found associated with human remains both in North and South America. Such findings indicate that they were trapped, killed and roasted by early man. Desiccated skins of these creatures have been found in caves of the southwestern United States, preserved by the dry air, and in Argentina a skin was found about 70 years ago apparently so fresh that it seemed there might be a chance that one species of the big ground sloth *Mylodon* was actually still alive.

The fragment of skin found, according to Florentino Ameghino, showed signs of having been exposed to the air for only a few months. It was partially discolored and the hair was coarse, stiff and of a reddish color fading into gray. Further searching discovered a cave which seemed to have been partially walled up in front with stones to form a sort of stable in which sloths had been kept. Sloth dung was thick in the cave, and there were many bones of the animals, as well as indications that they had been confined by humans. Argentine paleontologists theorized that Patagonian Indians kept the sloths as domestic animals, but whether the cave was used as a stable or was operated as a trap is still uncertain. In any event, no hope now remains of finding *Mylodon* alive.

As far as size is concerned, we know that South America's most spectacular animals are gone forever—the tapir is the biggest one still around. Yet of other types of animals, South America has some of the most dramatic known. Among its reptiles there are the anaconda, a huge watersnake of the great river basins, and the caiman, the alligator which stalks its tropical streams. It has some notable fishes: the arapaima is one of the biggest fresh-water fish known, up to 300 pounds in weight; and the piraibá, a giant catfish of the Amazon, grows up to six feet long with a weight of over 300 pounds. At the other extreme are the tiny but gaudy tropical fish so desired by aquarium lovers the world over—the neon tetra, the pencilfish and the fresh-water angelfish—as well as the fierce, meat-eating piranhas, which strip unwary victims swimming in their waters down to their bare bones.

Amphibians come in numberless and strange varieties. In the Amazon-Orinoco rain forest there are a host of frogs, most of which have learned in various ways to avoid the dangers that may lurk in the streams and rivers. When startled, some are said to jump not for the water, where the caimans lurk, but for the high grass. There are some varieties which lay their eggs in the crater of a tiny, volcano-shaped nest built out of mud: the eggs are protected from predatory fish while they hatch, and the young go through the entire metamorphosis from egg to frog inside the crater. Various types of frogs lay their eggs in trees—on leaves overhanging the water or in the water-storing cups of bromeliads and other epiphytic plants—and the metamorphosis from egg to baby frog takes place there. Others carry their eggs on their backs, where they are capped over during the hatching period. Lake Titicaca has a frog that lives in the cold depths and has long since lost its lungs, taking in oxygen through its skin; this flaccid creature, when hauled out on land, is so weak in the legs that it can only creep around. And still other frog species have skin which exudes a poison.

This, then, is South America, a continent of great diversity and singular interest in its flora and fauna. Some of its inhabitants are entirely local in origin, products of isolation which have survived. Others are the descendants of creatures which made their way there long before the land bridge was reestablished in the Pliocene, moving from island to island; and finally, there are the descendants of the northern immigrants. What we know today is a mixture of all these three, spread out in rain forest and mountain, desert and plain.

A WIND-TORN NOTHOFAGUS TREE MANAGES TO HANG ON IN PATAGONIA, THE SEMIARID LAND NEAR THE SOUTHERN TIP OF SOUTH AMERICA

Portrait of a Continent

Almost the size of the United States and Canada combined, South America is a land of surprising contrasts. Two thirds of it lies in the tropics, and here are found everything from rain forests to snow-capped mountains, and deserts so dry no plants grow in them. To the south are glaciers, grasslands, a cool, wind-swept desert and the moody, cloud-hidden islands of Tierra del Fuego.

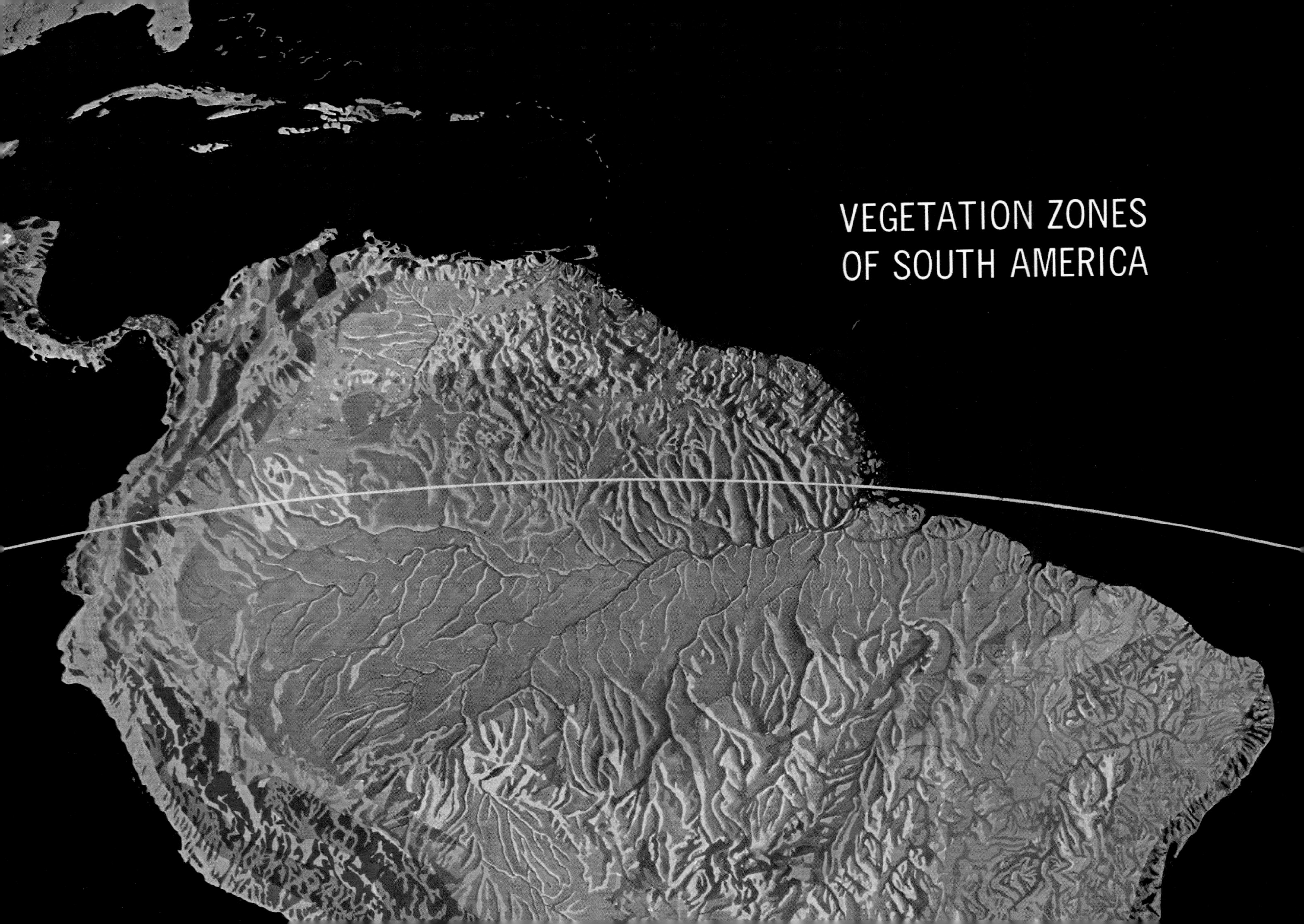

VEGETATION ZONES
OF SOUTH AMERICA

South America is essentially an enormous triangle with one of the world's longest mountain barriers running down its western edge, and the world's largest tropical rain forest and biggest river situated in its northern half. Wet winds sweep in from the Atlantic Ocean across this green basin, dumping great quantities of water on it. Farther to the south, the land is higher and the rains become progressively scantier, giving rise to semideciduous forest, savanna, prairie and finally semidesert in southern Argentina. But the winds and rains that supply this climate pattern to most of eastern South America cannot get across the barrier of the Andes. Largely because of this, a long strip of the western seacoast is a desert. South of the desert, however, moisture-laden winds blow in from the Pacific and produce a strip of dense forest. Similar forest also appears on mountain slopes near the equator. In the colder mountain regions all along the Andes chain lie montane meadow and taiga or tundra with vegetation like that of arctic lands. Near the southern tip of the continent is an area of permanent glacier.

RAIN FOREST

SEMIDECIDUOUS

SAVANNA SCRUB

PRAIRIE

TAIGA OR TUNDRA

DRY UPLAND

DRY LOW SCRUB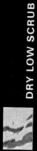

MONTANE MEADOW

SEMIDESERT

GLACIER

The Infernal South

Few areas of the world are more inhospitable than the southern tip of South America, a cloud-shrouded, storm-wracked land of such enormous frustration to the men who charted it that they gave its various parts bitter names like Deceit Island, Port Famine, Anxious Point, East and West Furies, Desolate Bay, Useless Bay. Hardly an hour goes by when the wind is not blowing, and few days pass without rain, sleet or snow; the rainfall in some places amounts to 18 feet a year. Temperatures remain fairly constant the year round, averaging 32°F. for the coldest month and 49°F. for the warmest at Ushuaia, the world's southernmost town. The cool, sodden summers help preserve the ancient glaciers that have given parts of the south their scarred look. Despite its monotonous climate, this land of winter poised perpetually on the brink of spring is not without a sullen beauty. The Andes emerge from the sea here, rising higher and higher as they snake up the west coast of the continent.

DEAD END OF THE CONTINENT, desolate islands like these fringe Tierra del Fuego. Here the zone of permanent snows begins at only 2,300 feet, and glaciers flow into the ocean.

RAKING CLOUDS some 8,000 feet above sea level, the Paine Mountains of southern Chile, part of the Andes, owe their odd shapes to glaciers that scoured the area in the ice age.

The Parched Lands

Bleak as Tierra del Fuego is, there are areas still more forbidding in South America, like the salty deserts *(right)* along 1,600 miles of Pacific coast. Driest of these is the mountainous Atacama of Chile, on parts of which rain fell in 1963 for the first time in the memory of man. Much of the Atacama consists of a hard material composed of sand and bits of rock cemented with salt. Long-dried-up lakes dot its expanses, but in its highest reaches there are a few that actually contain water. Rarely more than three or four feet deep, they are turquoise blue, emerald green, silver gray and even pink.

Another large dry area occurs farther south and east of the Andes in Patagonia *(below)*. The aridity of both regions has been brought about by similar phenomena—by the Andes which block the rain-bearing winds and by cold sea currents off the coasts. The currents chill the warm air blowing in from the oceans and cause sea fogs to form. They also stabilize the atmosphere and prevent rains from falling.

LAND WITHOUT RAIN, a stretch of desert north of Lima, Peru, lacks vegetation of any kind. Only on the distant slopes is there a smudge of green. This marks the loma zone, where the winter mist brushes up against the slopes and provides enough water to support a crop of quick-flowering plants and grasses.

HIGH AND DRY, the Patagonian plateau of Argentina is the only arid eastern coast below 40° south latitude. It is swept by winds which churn up dust and sand, cut down visibility and keep clouds in violent motion overhead. Occasional snows provide enough moisture to nurture stunted trees and short-lived grass.

23

The Many Faces of the Andes

Born of a folding and faulting of the earth's crust that began some 100 million years ago, the Andes are relatively young as mountain systems go, and betray it in the number of volcanoes that poke up among their peaks and the frequency with which earthquakes shake their roots. Stretching nearly 5,000 miles from Tierra del Fuego to the Caribbean, they pass through a variety of climatic zones and wear a variety of countenances. In Peru glaciers gleam on mountaintops (*below*), gorges plunge to depths almost twice that of the Grand Canyon, and Amazon tributaries course down eroded slopes (*left*) through a maze of ridges and deep ravines.

IZALCO VOLCANO in El Salvador is one of 83 active volcanoes in Latin America. It has erupted off and on since its birth in the early 17th Century, but has been asleep since 1958.

TEEP EASTERN SLOPES of the Andes near Machu Picchu in eru are heavily forested and watered by mists and rains pro-uced by upwellings of humid air from the tropical lowlands.

A SOURCE OF THE AMAZON is a string of lakes, like this one, high in Peru. Only 100 miles from the Pacific, they send their waters eastward on a 3,300-mile journey to the Atlantic.

NORTH OF ARGENTINA the rainfall increases and the deserts of the south gradually give way to enormous stretches of flat savanna. Of several types, these are spread widely through the central and northern parts of the continent. Shown here is the *pantanal* in southwestern Brazil, covering an area of 98,000 square miles. Relatively dry in winter, it gets some four feet of rain during the summer months, and at summer's end is an immense soggy marsh dotted with small hillocks of thickly forested higher and drier ground. Animals like the deer and agouti cluster on these hummocks during the late summer floods and make good hunting for the jaguars and pumas infesting the *pantanal*.

26

A FOREST ON A MOUNTAINSIDE IN SOUTHERN

GRAPPLING FOR SPACE, trees and plants in the Brazilian rain forest reflect the impetus given to growth by the damp, warm climate. Here summer is without end, leaves fall, flowers bloom, and fruits form and ripen at all times of the year.

THE GALLERY FOREST IS A STRIP OF DENSE

A Green Ocean

Of the different forests that grow in the lowlands of South America and on the mountains (*above*), the greatest by far is the rain forest. Like an ocean, it rolls from the Atlantic to the Andes and is even found snaking along riverbanks (*below*) into drier country. It is the most varied plant habitat in the world. A two-acre patch of typical growth will contain 30 or 40 different kinds of trees—compared to the five or six often found in mature deciduous woods of the United States. In a square mile of rain forest as many as 3,000 species of trees and shrubs have been identified. Temperatures are remarkably constant and, contrary to popular belief, not especially high. The highest recorded at Manaus, deep in the heart of Brazil, was 98.4°F.; the lowest 69.4°F., with the yearly average only 81.0°F.

A MEETING OF RIVERS takes place near Manaus, Brazil. Here the brown waters of the Amazon and the blue of the Rio Negro flow side by side before mixing many miles downstream.

The Journeying Waters

No river in the world carries a greater volume of water to the sea than the Amazon, nor does any other river drain so big an area—over two and a half million square miles, or somewhat less than half the South American continent. Fed by eight major rivers of more than 1,000 miles in length and by hundreds of smaller tributaries, it pours into the Atlantic 14 times as much water as the Mississippi disgorges into the Gulf of Mexico and does so with such force that it stains the Atlantic a mud-yellow up to 200 miles from the coast.

Called *O Rio Mar*—the River Sea—by the Brazilians, the Amazon is navigable by oceangoing ships as far as Iquitos at the foothills of the Andes, 2,300 miles inland. Between the months of November and June, it overflows its banks and spreads out onto a flood plain 50 to 60 miles wide, dislodging great chunks of earth and sweeping them, sometimes with animals on them, toward the sea. So mighty is the Amazon, that it dwarfs the other major river systems in South America and makes even rivers like the one opposite seem positively insignificant.

DROPPING 741 FEET from an escarpment in British Guiana, the Potaro River forms one of the world's great waterfalls—almost five times higher than Niagara.

THE HOWLER, surly and sluggish
in manner, is one of the few New
World monkeys that have not been
tamed by the Indians. It is, instead, hunted by them. Sometimes
a wounded one dies and hangs out
of reach, its prehensile tail wound
around a branch in a death grip.

2

Acrobats
in the Treetops

ALL monkeys are fascinating, but for me the South American species are particularly interesting, probably because I know them best. My acquaint-
ance is based on disease—we were studying jungle yellow fever in Colombia
and we kept seven different kinds of monkeys in the laboratory regularly. I
became greatly impressed with the character differences among them; often I
wished I could stop studying disease and start studying monkeys, but there
was not time for both. I hated taking blood samples from the monkeys and I
hated even more to infect them with a disease that might well be fatal. But
how else could we find out about yellow fever?

Monkeys that recovered from the infection were turned loose on the laboratory grounds, and many of them stayed there. Visiting scientists, I noticed, were
more interested in the monkeys than in any other aspect of the laboratory, and
I solved the visitor problem by giving them chairs so they could sit in our bam-
boo grove and watch monkeys.

The American monkeys are just as fascinating for the student of evolution
as they are for the visitor at the zoo. To the casual observer, the New and
the Old World monkeys look rather alike—at least they are all "monkeys."

But in actual fact they have experienced quite separate evolutionary histories.

According to the latest count, there are 64 American species, classified into 16 different genera. As far back as we have been able to trace the fossil record, the New World and Old World monkeys seem to have been descending separately. Somewhere far, far back, there may be a common prosimian ancestor, but these separate heritages go back at least to the Eocene. There is no evidence that primates existed in South America before it was isolated, so they did not originate there. But fossil finds of lemur- and tarsier-like animals in North America suggest that the New World monkeys evolved from these ancestors, moving down through Central America and reaching the isolated southern continent by island-hopping, probably in the Oligocene—a belief borne out by late Oligocene primate fossils discovered in Patagonia. It is clear, in any event, that they are not newcomers to the continent, in the sense of having arrived after the reestablishment of the land bridge.

THE New World primates all have three premolar teeth, while the Old World monkeys and apes, like man, have only two. The nose is constructed quite differently: the American monkeys tend to have a very wide partition between the nostrils, which are thus directed sideways rather than forward and downward as in Old World species. Many Old World monkeys—the baboons, for example—have naked and garishly colored rumps. This is never the case with American species. On the other hand, no Old World monkey has a prehensile tail, though several of the New World species do. Any monkey that can hang by its tail, then, is American.

These and other lines of evidence indicate that the Neotropical primates have long been isolated from their Old World relatives—that the New World species are all more related to each other than to any of the Old World groups. The differences among the South American forms must all be the consequence of evolution on the isolated island continent. They differ enough among themselves to be classified in two families, the Callithricidae, or marmosets, and the Cebidae, or monkeys proper. Unfortunately, however, our knowledge of their behavior is mostly based on the observation of captive specimens or on chance encounters by traveling scientists. Careful study in the wild is not easy, because they are all arboreal forest animals—much more at home in the forest environment than visiting humans—and when alarmed, they manage easily enough to stay out of sight. Several species are highly prized as meat by local people and often shot at, which has made the survivors extremely shy. One of the few exceptions to this situation is offered by Barro Colorado Island in Panama, where not only the primates but all other forms of wildlife have been protected from hunting for many years.

When the Chagres River was dammed in the course of the construction of the Panama Canal, some 165 square miles of lowlands were flooded, forming Gatun Lake—the midsection of the canal. Many hills in the river valley thus became islands in a fresh-water lake. Barro Colorado is the largest of these islands, with an area of 3,840 acres. In 1923 this island was set aside as a nature reserve and biological laboratory, and has been maintained as such ever since. Much of it is covered with undisturbed rain forest, and parts that had been cleared are slowly reverting to original forest conditions.

The island is large enough to support populations of most of the Panama rain-forest animals. The mammals in particular, undisturbed by hunting since the establishment of the laboratory, can be observed there in the wild more easily than anywhere else in tropical America. The island, accessible and yet protected, is thus an ideal place for studies of animal behavior—though such studies, in the complex vegetation of a rain forest which is still in effect a virgin wilderness, remain difficult enough.

The most conspicuous monkeys on Barro Colorado are the howlers, which are also the second-largest South American species. In most other places they are hunted enough to make them extremely wary of humans. Even on Barro Colorado they could hardly be called friendly, but they can at least be observed, and they have formed the subject of the most thorough and detailed study yet to be made of any American monkey in its natural habitat.

A psychologist, C. R. Carpenter, spent a total of eight months on the island in 1931, 1932 and 1933, going out every day with field glasses and notebook to watch the howler monkeys. In the course of the months, he became fairly intimately acquainted with them—especially with the members of a band living near the laboratory, on which he concentrated for observations of behavior.

Since this classic study, Carpenter and his colleagues have followed up their original observations with two other large-scale studies, gaining further insights into howler behavior and compiling some interesting figures which show wide fluctuations in the howler population of the island. Between 1933 and 1951, for example, the howlers diminished by half, to less than 250 animals, probably because of a yellow fever epidemic. But the monkeys quickly rebuilt their population and in 1959 were up over the 800 mark. In the absence of man as a predator, it is disease, and not other predators, that seems to be the big regulator of howler populations.

Carpenter's pioneering work of the 1930s established that the monkey population of the island was divided into distinct groups, or clans, with each group restricted to a limited area within the island forest. These ranges overlapped, and when two clans happened to come near each other, there would be a loud vocal battle, kept up until one clan or the other retreated. Howlers are among the noisiest members of the animal kingdom. The whole larynx is much enlarged, with the hyoid bone of the throat forming a sort of boxlike resonator, larger in the male than in the female, but present in both sexes. A howling chorus can be heard for at least a mile.

THERE are various, quite obvious reasons for this vocalization. Certainly, as Carpenter observed, it serves to mark out territories—and vocal battles would seem a less damaging way of defending a territory than physical combat. The approach of a possible enemy, like one of the big cats, is also greeted with a howling chorus. The howls can be frightening enough. During the period I lived on Barro Colorado, I got into the habit of imitating the howls whenever I found myself near a clan, and the monkeys invariably responded. A gnome-like old male, coming fairly close and howling back with obvious anger, could be quite scary, despite my knowledge that howlers do not attack. Yet it would seem that the monkeys are protected as much by their agility and group coordination as by their noisemaking ability. Dawn, each morning, is usually greeted with howling choruses, and occasional sporadic outbursts of howling during the day, started by older males, have a definite social function in keeping the groups spaced well apart in their various territories.

The average howler clan on Barro Colorado consisted of three adult males and seven or eight adult females, with associated young, making a total of 17 or 18 individuals. Within the clans, Carpenter found relations generally peaceful

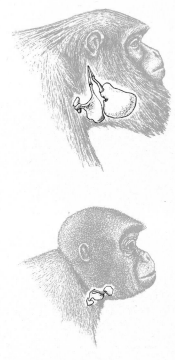

HOW A HOWLER HOWLS

The loudest of the New World monkeys, and certainly one of the noisiest animals for its size anywhere, is the howler. Its roar, beginning as a pumping growl that bursts into a series of drumlike booms, can be heard as far as a mile. The sound originates in the larynx but is greatly amplified by the bony sound box—the hyoid apparatus—in the howler's neck (top), nearly 25 times as big as that of the similar-sized woolly monkey (bottom). The roar is produced when the howler contracts its chest and stomach muscles, forcing air under pressure across an opening at the top of the sound box.

among the individuals, except for playful competition among the young and occasional sharp conflicts, quickly terminated, between adults. He did not find that any particular male served as "leader," dominating the others, though subsequent observations appear to contradict this. He saw no signs of sexual jealousy: the initiative, with a female in heat, seemed to lie with the female, who chose the male with whom she wished to mate—and when he was sated, moved on to another mate.

In addition to the clans, Carpenter found a number of solitary "bachelor" males on the island. Some of these apparently would just drift away from a group for a while, and then would rejoin this same group again without much difficulty. But sometimes a bachelor male, apparently approaching a strange clan, would be greeted by disapproving howls—tolerance did not extend to outsiders. In one case, Carpenter watched the persistent attempts of a bachelor to join a clan over a period of several months, with eventual success.

Howler monkeys are purely vegetarian, eating a tremendous variety of leaves, fruits, nuts and seeds, and they spend between four and six hours a day in feeding. They are greatly aided by their prehensile tails: often they swing by them, nibbling leaves and fruit directly from the stems on which they grow, pulling the food toward them rather than picking it and holding it in their hands. They are prodigal in their eating habits, too, sometimes taking only a single bite and then passing on to a new and tempting offer. They seem to get from leaves and fruits not only the nourishment they need but also water. In any event, they do not appear to have to come down to the ground to drink, and after a heavy rain they have been seen to lick water from leaves or even collect it in their hands as it runs down from the trees.

Unlike some of the other American primates, howler bands in the wild never associate with bands of other species. Within their own societies they have been characterized as "democratic." In fact, the late Earnest Hooton, Harvard University's colorful anthropologist, has referred to the New World monkeys in general as "democrats and proletarians" in contrast to what he termed the "totalitarian monkeys of the Old World." "There can be no doubt," he wrote, "of the contrast between these widely separated monkey groups in their social characteristics. If you have any fascist leanings you will prefer macaques and baboons to howlers and spider monkeys, but if you are democratic or communistic you will share my partiality for American monkey institutions."

Howlers have about the widest range of any of the American monkeys, extending from southern Mexico to Paraguay and tropical Argentina. They differ considerably in color from place to place, ranging from black to golden yellow, and this, along with anatomical differences, has led zoologists to classify them as five different species of the genus *Alouatta*. The other monkeys with pre-

HOWLERS OUT ON A LIMB

When howlers move from tree to tree, they do so by marching single file over their regular highways—the branches. Frequently they use the same routes, and often take the same order on the line of march, with a large, mature male usually leading the way and another male bringing up the rear. Occasionally, a young howler will briefly bound ahead and assume first place as in this drawing. The females follow behind the leader, but those carrying babies usually stay toward the rear. Frisky, bold juveniles, newly independent of their mothers, are scattered throughout the column. By emitting a deep clucking sound, any of the mature males can start up a march.

hensile tails are species of *Cebus* (capuchins), *Lagothrix* (woolly monkeys), *Ateles* (spider monkeys) and *Brachyteles* (woolly spider monkeys).

Capuchins are probably the most familiar of American primates—they are the monkeys of the organ grinders. They have almost as wide a distribution as the howlers, ranging from Honduras south to Paraguay and the Misiones Province of Argentina. As with howlers, individuals from different parts of this range differ considerably in appearance, so that they are ordinarily classified into four species, each with a number of geographical races.

Capuchins are hardy animals and they do better in captivity than any of the other American monkeys. As a result, they may be seen in nearly every zoo. Anyone watching a capuchin for any length of time gets the idea that it is a very "intelligent" animal, and this has led to a number of elaborate studies of behavior. These studies seem to indicate that capuchins are about the brightest of subhuman animals. Their only real rivals in this respect are the chimpanzees; whether chimps or capuchins are brighter is a matter for further study, but it is interesting in itself that they are both so close. We expect the great apes to be more intelligent than other animals because they are man's closest living relatives. But that one of the American monkeys, so distantly related to the human line, should be so clever is surprising.

Cleverness, of course, is not always desirable in pets. An elderly capuchin named Roberta was one of the long-term fixtures of the yellow fever laboratory in Colombia. Roberta was endlessly amusing, but her antics could also at times be trying. She seemed to take particular delight in annoying visiting scientists by snatching things from their pockets and then being coy about giving them up. I remember that she once brazenly seized the spectacles from the nose of a distinguished visitor, ran up a tree and sat there dangling them—while he thought about the distance across the mountains to the nearest oculist. The spectacles, by some miracle, were recovered intact, but we were not always so fortunate with Roberta's tricks.

Capuchins are particularly good at manipulating objects—using tools—which led Hooton to call them "monkey mechanics." Capuchin behavior, in fact, illustrates beautifully the whole idea of "monkeying."

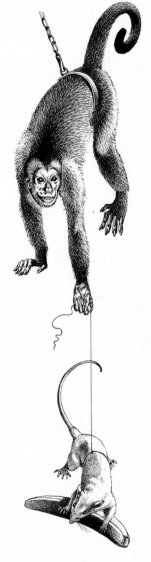

THE CLEVER CAPUCHIN

The capuchin is generally considered to be the smartest of the New World monkeys. An experiment conducted by Dr. Heinrich Klüver at the University of Chicago bears this out. A hungry monkey was tied out of reach of a banana. It took only half a minute to grab a string attached to a rat, which had been set loose in the room earlier. Then it tossed the rat over the banana while holding onto the string, and as soon as the rat clutched the banana, hauled them both in. When the experiment was repeated with a stringless rat, the capuchin held it by the tail and again got the banana.

THE most extensive laboratory experiments with capuchin behavior have been made by the psychologist Heinrich Klüver at the University of Chicago. Klüver's cleverest capuchin not only quickly learned to use all sorts of tools to get at food but also solved many problems requiring the use of more than one tool. For instance, she used a wire hook to get hold of a short T-stick which served to knock down a long T-stick which enabled her to pull in the food. She also learned to "make" tools in the sense of tearing off pieces of newspaper and rolling them up to serve as a rake, or, for a similar purpose, breaking off sticks that had been fastened to a table.

Klüver showed moving pictures to various Old and New World monkeys— but only the capuchins showed clear and definite reactions. The clever female used in the tool experiments would watch the films with great attention and chatter excitedly at incidents that interested her. When an African python appeared in the picture, she displayed signs of extreme fear, defecating and disappearing into a corner of the room where the picture could not be seen.

Some of the South American monkeys are quite striking in appearance, and one of these is the woolly monkey, so named for its thick, teddy-bear-like coat. Woolly monkeys were unknown to European scientists until Alexander von

37

Humboldt came across them in the course of his journey along the Orinoco River in 1800. They are common enough in many parts of the forests of the upper Amazon and Orinoco rivers. Their habits apparently are similar to those of howlers but they are somewhat smaller in size. Woolly monkeys most commonly travel in groups of from 12 to 25 individuals, though occasionally there may be as many as 50 in a group. They are largely vegetarian, living on fruits and leaves. In captivity, however, they will eat both cooked and raw meat. Their voracious appetite is notorious. and local people have with good reason given them the common name of *barrigudo*, or "potbelly."

The prehensile tail reaches its greatest development in the spider monkeys, the acrobats of the tropical American forests. Their only rivals as trapeze artists are the gibbons of the tropical Orient, and the gibbons have to make do without any tail. The tail of a spider monkey is very much an extra hand. Longer even than their incredibly long arms, it is often used in reaching for things as well as in climbing. The underside of the tip has bare, ridged skin, like the palm of a hand, extending up to one third the length of the tail. It is so sensitive that it can pick up objects as small as a pea. The hands themselves are almost awkward by comparison—they have no thumbs or at most only stumps, and the four fingers cannot be opened fully, being bent into a hook-like position by their very short tendons. Spider monkeys even "hold tails" instead of holding hands; young ones in particular are often seen with their tails intertwined with that of their mother. With the help of their tails, and by using their hands for swinging and their feet for climbing, they can move through the trees at about the same speed as a man walking very fast on the ground.

Spider monkeys, like the howlers, range north along the Gulf of Mexico as far as Vera Cruz, but they do not extend as far south as the howlers or the capuchins, being restricted to the Amazon basin. They are largely vegetarian, living chiefly on fruits and nuts. They are social, being found most often in bands of from 10 to 30 individuals, but from the studies of Carpenter and others it has been established that the bands are not as tightly organized as are those of the howlers. Carpenter found some groups within the band composed of males only, apparently bachelors temporarily banding together, others of females and young, and still others with males, females and young all living happily together. A given band would stay in the same territory for weeks, and the spider monkeys would defend their territory just as lustily as the howlers.

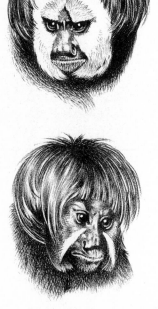

MONKEY FACES—HIS AND HERS

Although the males and females of most species of New World monkeys look alike, there are species in which strong secondary sexual characteristics set the sexes apart. Among the white-headed sakis of northeastern South America, the male's face (top) has a masklike mat of hard whitish hair, in contrast to the female's (bottom), which is black and almost naked, except for long pale yellow whiskers. These differences are blurred toward the periphery of the species' range. In one direction the females look increasingly like the males, and in the other the males resemble the mustached females.

THE most rarely seen of all the South American primates is the woolly spider monkey, a probably vanishing species of the rain forests of Tupi Province in eastern Brazil. This interesting creature is even larger than a howler monkey, with a thick coat and a thick, extremely long, prehensile tail. Almost nothing is known of its habits; for all of its size, it is a wary animal, seldom seen in the wild and with a very restricted range.

All of the South American primates so far discussed have prehensile tails; the remaining monkey forms—the douroucoulis, also called the owl or night monkeys, the titis, the sakis, the uakaris and the squirrel monkeys—do not. This is the most obvious characteristic linking them as a group, but there is also one big difference among them: alone among the American monkeys, the douroucoulis are truly nocturnal.

Living at night, of course, demands its own adaptations as well as providing its own rewards. Douroucoulis can tap the rich food supply of night-flying insects with no competition from their daytime cousins, and they also eat fruit.

For their nocturnal existence they have developed enormous eyes which provide keen vision in dim light, and their hearing is keen as well, so that they can find their way expertly around the dark forest. Their range extends from Panama to as far south as Paraguay and northeast Argentina.

With this single exception of the nocturnal douroucoulis, American monkeys in general are curiously similar in their habits—although it must also be admitted that this apparent similarity may well be a consequence of our ignorance of many of the details of their lives. But as far as we know, they are all arboreal, most of them coming to the ground only rarely and reluctantly. They also seem to have somewhat similar food habits, eating leaves, fruits, insects and such other small animals as they can catch. Howlers are different in that they are exclusively vegetarian and mostly leaf eaters at that, and it seems that spider and woolly monkeys eat more vegetable material than most of the others. But the similarities are certainly more striking than the differences, and this is brought out by the frequency with which different species are seen associating together, apparently carrying out the same sort of activities.

TITIS are small and long-haired, and actually resemble in many ways the other side of the family tree, the marmosets; but their hands, feet and nails place them among the cebids. They are prominent noisemakers in the forest, being almost as loud as the howlers but on a higher pitch, with an occasional whistling note. Among their marmosetlike attributes are that the males often carry the young and that most species are brightly colored. Red is the predominant color in most species, sometimes with a yellow face or a strongly contrasting blaze of white or black across the forehead.

The squirrel monkeys, or saimiris, are the smallest of the cebid monkeys. They are also among the commonest of the Neotropical primates, ranging from Costa Rica to the Amazon basin. They travel in large troops sometimes consisting of more than a hundred individuals, very visible in the jungle, several troops at times being in the same section of forest at once. They always stay close to a riverbank, among trees that are loaded with flower and fruit-bearing creepers. And through constant use they make pathways through the tangles of vines, along which they troop in single-file, follow-the-leader style.

Despite the fact that squirrel monkeys' tails are not prehensile, they are useful in more ways than just as a balancing organ. The animals have been observed resting, with the tail, which is long and thick, brought forward between the legs and wrapped up around the back and shoulders as if for warmth. In fact, at night the squirrel monkeys cuddle close together, sometimes fighting to see who will get the favored, the warmest, spot in the center.

Squirrel monkeys are popular pets with local people everywhere they occur, and are frequently seen around native houses, often riding on the backs of dogs —the two kinds of pets get along well with each other. Since they are so frequently and easily tamed, they turn up more often in pet shops than any other American monkey. They are undeniably charming animals; the black of their lips and nostrils making them look as if they had just been exploring some inkpot. They are always active and alert, and certainly give the impression of being intelligent. They are rather delicate creatures, however, and do not do as well in northern climates as their relatives, the tougher capuchins.

The marmosets are distinguished from the cebids by their smaller size and squirrel-like appearance, by the usual absence of the third molar tooth so that they have 32 instead of 36 teeth, and by having claws instead of nails on the fingers and toes—except that the short great toe has a flat nail. These character-istics, however, are not always clear, and some experts argue that the marmosets are not different enough from the cebids to be treated as a separate family.

The marmosets are in the main creatures of the South American rain forests. Only one species, Geoffroy's tamarin, gets as far north as Panama and neighbor-ing parts of Costa Rica. Because they are so strictly forest animals, where condi-tions for observation are difficult, most of what we know about their habits in the wild is based on the incidental observations of traveling naturalists or of animal collectors. Some kinds of marmosets have long been popular pets, and a number of people have succeeded in getting them to breed in captivity. They are just beginning to get attention from psychologists: their habit of consistently produc-ing two young at a birth makes them interesting subjects for comparative stud-ies, and their small size permits laboratories to keep large numbers of them.

Many of the marmosets have very limited distributions. This seems to be due to their reluctance to leave the trees. Rivers, for instance, are effective barriers. Marmosets can swim well enough if thrown into the water, but they are not willingly adventurous. Their very local habits may well be the explanation of the profusion of marmoset forms: some five genera and 36 species are recog-nized. Isolated from each other by rivers and open country, the different pop-ulations developed different characteristics, and when later in the course of geological history they did happen to come in contact, they may have been different enough so that they could not interbreed.

THE various marmosets seem to be even more similar to each other in hab-its than the cebid monkeys. As with the cebids, different species are often seen associating together in the wild, and they also live well together in captivity. They are often compared with the tree squirrels as far as their size and habits are concerned. Like squirrels, they use their claws for clinging to bark, and they also have a squirrel-like tendency to rest with their belly on a tree branch with the legs hanging down limply on either side. At least one species has the habit of sliding down branches on its belly. Their movements tend to be quick and jerky, like the movements of tree lizards, and they scamper about the trees in a very squirrel-like fashion.

All marmosets are social: in captivity they tend to huddle together, and if kept alone they obviously enjoy human companionship or that of other kinds of mon-keys. In the wild they normally travel in groups usually of 10 or more individuals.

Insects and eggs are the chief food of marmosets, and captive animals show great dexterity in stalking and catching things like flies. They eat spiders, worms and a variety of insects with great relish, and since the tropical forest abounds in such creatures, they have no food problems. They also eat seeds and fruits in the wild, and in captivity they will eat a considerable variety of vegetable ma-terials like fruits, nuts, roots and even bread crumbs and biscuits. They do not thrive in captivity, however, unless given some form of animal protein.

The small size, charming manners and fierce appearance of the marmosets have made them favorite pets at least since Shakespeare's day, when they were often carried about by ladies of fashion in their sleeves. They did not, however, thrive under the untropical conditions of Elizabethan English houses, and con-sequently have long been regarded as very delicate pets. Actually, as a group they are hardier than the cebid monkeys, being less prone to respiratory diseases, and with proper attention to temperature, sunlight, food, cleanliness and exer-cise they do well in captivity—in fact, some have lived as long as 16 years.

MOST FAMILIAR OF THE SOUTH AND CENTRAL AMERICAN MONKEYS, THE PLAYFUL CAPUCHIN IS ALSO THOUGHT TO BE THE MOST INTELLIGENT

The New World Monkeys

Although they superficially resemble some of their cousins in Africa and Asia, the 64 species of New World monkeys are actually quite different. They tend to be small. They all live in trees in the tropical forest, having developed no ground-dwelling or open-country species. As a group, they are exceptionally acrobatic, and some of them have prehensile tails, the only monkeys so endowed.

MANED MARMOSETS
Genus *Leontideus*

TAMARINS
Genus *Saguinus*

CALLIMICOS
Genus *Callimico*

DOUROUCOULIS
Genus *Aotus*

TITIS
Genus *Callicebus*

TRUE
MARMOSETS
Genus *Callithrix*

SQUIRREL MONKEYS
Genus *Saimiri*

PYGMY
MARMOSETS
Genus *Cebuella*

M A R M O S E T S

C E B I D M O N K E Y S

A FAMILY TREE

OF AMERICAN

MONKEYS

PLATYR-
RHINES

Here is the family tree of the New World
monkeys, or platyrrhines. They are divided into two families, as indicated by
the big fork in the trunk—marmosets
at the left and cebids at the right.
The marmosets and cebids differ in several striking ways. The marmosets move

SAKIS
Genus *Pithecia*

UAKARIS
Genus *Cacajao*

HOWLERS
Genus *Alouatta*

WOOLLY MONKEYS
Genus *Lagothrix*

CAPUCHINS
Genus *Cebus*

SPIDER MONKEYS
Genus *Ateles*

like squirrels, running and scrambling through the branches, aided by their clawlike nails; the cebids tend to leap or swing from tree to tree. The marmosets are the smallest primates in the New World, the tiniest being the pygmy marmoset, ·which measures three to four inches without its tail. The cebids are a larger and more highly diversified family than the marmosets and may be separated into two categories: those with prehensile tails and those without. In this painting, four of the five prehensile-tailed genera are shown on the branches that arise farthest to the right. Other outstanding cebids are the uakaris, which have the shortest tails of any New World monkey; the sakis, which have the bushiest; and the only completely nocturnal monkey, the shy and huge-eyed douroucouli.

MUSTACHED TAMARINS MAKE GOOD PETS: KEPT BY INDIANS OF THE AMAZON VALLEY, THEY PICK PARASITES FROM THEIR MASTERS' SCALPS

The Marmosets

The Lilliputians of the monkey kingdom, the marmosets are amusing-looking creatures with beady eyes, prominent ears, long tails and thick fur that gives some of them comical head tufts and enormous, droopy, Otto von Bismarck mustaches. Un-like the other New World monkeys, the marmosets have "claws" instead of nails on all their fingers and toes except the big toe. And whereas the other monkeys usually give birth to one baby at a time, marmosets habitually have two and sometimes even

COTTON TOPS, AMONG THE FIRST SOUTH AMERICAN MONKEYS SENT TO EUROPE, HAVE THE MOST BIRDLIKE VOICES OF ALL THE MARMOSETS

three babies. A further peculiarity is that the father often cares for the young, carrying them about with him all day long, except at feeding time, when he hands them over to the female.

The marmosets have high-pitched voices and are known to make a great variety of sounds, including twitterings, chirpings and squeakings that strongly suggest conversation. Perched on branches high in the trees, where they can be heard but not seen, they are sometimes mistaken by the uninitiated for birds.

45

A SAKI, face in profile, displays the shaggy coat and tail that camouflage it in the jungle. When resting on its favorite perch, the crotch of a tree, it looks like a lump of withered vegetation.

A RED UAKARI, caught in a placid moment, sits in a cradle of branches. When disturbed or excited, this species blushes a vivid scarlet and emits loud shouts that sound like laughter.

Some Cebids—the Sakis and Uakaris

The cebids fall into two distinct groups—those with tails that can seize and grasp, and those with tails that cannot. Among the latter are the strange little monkeys shown here. The uakaris *(upper right and opposite)* are the only primates in tropical America with short tails. In the ranks of the Old World monkeys, such brevity usually indicates terrestrial habits, but the uakaris keep to the trees, never descending to the ground. Their tails are short not because the vertebrae are fewer in number but because they are smaller and in an evolutionarily degenerate condition. The sakis *(upper left)*, on the other hand, are distinguished by the length and bushiness of their tails, the long, coarse hair of which is often wavy. They use their tails for balance as they walk on all fours through the treetops.

OUTSIZE TEETH of a black uakari from northern South America seem to indicate a meat diet and a fierce disposition, but in fact all uakaris are vegetarians and rather timid. Even when cornered, they rarely make use of their fangs. Lacking opposable thumbs, uakaris use these tusklike lower canines and long incisors as tools—they peel and tear fruit with them.

47

A Monkey with Five Limbs

Of all the prehensile-tailed cebids, the nimblest by far is the spider monkey. Not only is its tail longer than its thin, spidery legs and arms, but it actually functions as a fifth limb. The tail seems to be always in motion, the highly sensitive tip coiling and uncoiling, ever ready to probe for and pick up an object or to reach out and grab a branch. These photographs of a loose-jointed young spider monkey in action demonstrate the versatility of the tail —providing support while the hooklike hands are moving along a branch or dangling free, acting as a balance and sometimes an anchor *(bottom right)*.

3

The Old Inhabitants

EVERYONE knows something about opossums—that they play dead when alarmed, that they have large families and bad tempers, that they are eaten only by the poor, or perhaps even that they are marsupials and thus American relatives of kangaroos and their like in Australia. Except in folklore, they are not much admired. This is probably a mistake, because certainly opossums are successful animals if success is measured in terms of abundance or extent of range—they occur throughout the Americas from Argentina to the northern United States, and in recent years they have been pushing still farther north from New England and the Middle West into Canada. Even civilization has proved no barrier to them: they are among the few wild animals that get along with man, living on garbage not only in the suburbs but also occasionally venturing into cities.

The common opossum so familiar to us in the United States is called *Didelphis marsupialis*. We have long since accepted it as part of our fauna—so long that few people realize that this sturdy creature is really a northern invader from South America, where it is still abundant. And a sturdy animal it is indeed: it has not only survived the invasion of northern placental mammals into

South America but has competed successfully with the invaders on their home grounds, in a different environment, in colder temperatures and with different food. *Didelphis marsupialis* is unquestionably a quite indestructible mammal.

In tropical America, however, *Didelphis marsupialis* is still only one of a family of 11 genera classified in the family Didelphidae. One of these is *Didelphis azarae*, a species whose two races look very similar to the opossum we know. All the others can be called opossums only if the word is used in a broad sense, since most of them would not be recognized as such by North Americans. In contrast to the common concept of the opossum, they are often strikingly handsome little creatures, particularly those which live in the tropical forest. The most abundant are members of the genus *Marmosa*, more informally known as "mouse opossums," of which the most recent study lists 37 different species.

Marmosas are about the size of small rats, and their fur is rich, sleek and usually a warm, attractive brown. Almost all of them live in the tropical rain forest, and in those moist, green depths they lead a life which is so secluded that much of their history and many of their habits are still unknown. As with many South American animals, we know more or less how many kinds there are, but much remains to be discovered of how they differ in habits and habitats.

For example, it seems likely that most marmosas feed chiefly on insects, but like their larger opossum relatives they will, if need be, eat almost anything they can find. In captivity they take to fruit and cheese and lick the salt from salted nuts. They particularly like bananas, which make an effective bait for trapping them and also still serve occasionally to transport them north to U.S. seaports. In earlier years a good many marmosas used to arrive in North America hidden in bunches of bananas, until the practice of dipping the fruit in water before loading it was adopted. This flushed out most of the accidental stowaways.

Where do marmosas live in the tropical forest? That is not always easy to discover, since they are strictly nocturnal and spend the day in hiding. Some make their nests high up in trees; others will use any convenient place, like a hole in a tree, an abandoned bird nest or even—as the zoologist Robert K. Enders discovered when studying mammalian habits on Barro Colorado Island —nest boxes put out for birds. And, of course, the reason they get carried away in banana bunches is because they also nest in them. Marsupial fashion, they bear their young when they are little more than embryos, but they have no pouch and the babies grow while clinging to the teats which nourish them.

SHARING the many advantages of life in the rain forest, with its lush growth, its hordes of busy insects and its almost unlimited opportunities for concealment, are a few larger relatives of the marmosas—the woolly opossums and two types of so-called "four-eyed" opossums. These latter get their name from two distinctive white spots, circled in dark fur, just above their real eyes. What the function of these markings is no one yet knows, but it might be theorized that they serve to startle or confuse would-be predators.

The woolly opossums, like most of the Didelphidae, are primarily insect eaters but are adaptable enough to eat fruit as well. With their dense, soft, gray fur, they are particularly attractive animals and look as though they would make charming pets, but unfortunately their tempers are apt to be bad and they are inclined to snarl and spit at the approach of a human.

All of these opossums—in fact, all but one of the Didelphidae—have the prehensile tails so characteristic of Neotropical species. This suggests a long history of life in forests which are seasonally flooded, making life impossible on the ground, and in fact the marmosas and their relatives are among South America's oldest oldtimers. But they are not all tree dwellers. The one species which does not have a prehensile tail is the world's only aquatic marsupial, the water opossum, *Chironectes*, which long ago elected to stay on the ground and cope with the floods. As one consequence, it developed webbed feet, which help make it an expert swimmer and diver.

Chironectes poses some interesting questions. Its fur, covering its short, foot-long body, is dense, gray and seal-like—clearly an adaptation to aquatic existence. But what does the female do with her young when she dives? Some believe that she may trap air in her pouch and close it tightly for the duration of her underwater forays for the crustaceans which she eats. Possibly the tiny young can get along for limited periods without air. It may even be that when she is carrying young she does not feed in the water but reverts to a terrestrial existence. The water opossum lives in burrows along the banks of streams, but it can climb, though its long, thick, naked tail has lost its prehensile abilities and serves only as a balancing organ.

A SUBMERSIBLE MARSUPIAL

The gray and black water opossum, the world's only aquatic marsupial, lives along riverbanks in wooded areas ranging from Guatemala to southern Brazil. A night feeder, it emerges at dusk from its burrow at the river's edge and dives for frogs, fish and shellfish. Among its adaptations for a life in the water are webbed hind feet and a short, dense coat of fur covering its foot-long body. The female carries her babies around with her in an abdominal pouch, but how she keeps them from smothering or drowning if she dives with them remains unknown.

THERE is—in addition to the opossums and a few tiny, shrewlike marsupials which live among the litter on the forest floor—another family of South American marsupials called the Caenolestidae. These are not rain forest animals but dwellers of the more temperate woodlands along the slopes of the Andes. The three known types are different enough from each other so that each is classified in a separate genus: *Caenolestes*, *Lestoros* and *Rhyncholestes*. All are small, ratlike animals of very undistinguished appearance, but they are fascinating creatures to the zoologist because they are closely allied to certain extinct forms and because they possess characteristics which identify them as surviving members of a highly differentiated and presumably much more numerous group. Detailed knowledge of this group could throw light on the origin and dispersal of marsupials generally.

Curiously little is known about them. The first specimen, mentioned in a list of the mammals of Ecuador in 1860, was described as "shrewlike." This first account passed virtually unnoticed until, in 1895, a second specimen turned up in a collection coming to the British Museum. It was immediately recognized to be a very special sort of marsupial, different in tooth and toe arrangement from any of the other living forms of America or Australia. In the present century, more specimens have been collected in the high mountain forests of Peru, Ecuador, Colombia and Venezuela. In 1923, a species later named *Rhyncholestes raphanurus* was found in the heavy temperate forests of Chiloé Island off Chile; in 1939 a specimen of this same species was collected on the Chilean mainland at an altitude of 3,000 feet, under deep growth in a cool, moist forest. From an examination of the stomach contents, it appears that these animals feed chiefly on insects, though they have also been caught in traps baited with small birds.

These 11 genera of Didelphidae and three of Caenolestidae are the last survivors of what was once an impressive and varied host of marsupials which exploited virtually all environments of South America. That they survived the invasion of the more advanced placentals from the north is probably due in part to their environment—the rich world of the forest with its many possibilities of making a living and keeping out of a predator's way—and certainly partly to the innate toughness of the animals themselves.

No less tough and persistent are the members of the other order of oldtimers, the Edentata, which includes those rather more conspicuous creatures, the sloths, anteaters and armadillos. The sloths are among the real curiosities of the animal world—they literally spend most of their lives upside down. There are two kinds of sloths, the *Choloepus*, with two claws on its forelimbs, and the *Bradypus*, with three (both types have three claws on their hind limbs). These claws are truly extraordinary: long, tapering and permanently hooked, they are strongly reminiscent of the baling hooks used by longshoremen in loading cargo. While most animals walk on their feet, the sloths hang by theirs, with the curved claws holding them so firmly to a tree branch that it is impossible to pull them down even when they are dead—they must be lifted up first to loosen their hold.

Although sloths move every bit as slowly as their name implies, they do so with great sure-footedness. They have no prehensile tails to help them; in fact, they have hardly any tails at all. On the ground, they are so awkward as to be almost helpless, but surprisingly, they can swim: if a branch from which one is hanging should break, dropping the animal into the water, it somehow gets ashore using the same excruciatingly slow motion of the limbs which transports it through the trees. Experimentally, sloths have even been held under water for as much as 30 minutes without drowning.

To see a sloth making its way hand over hand through the branches of a tree is to observe a phenomenon of locomotion found nowhere else in the animal kingdom. Archie Carr, the noted turtle expert, once spent five days watching sloths in a Costa Rican town while he waited for an airplane. "Nothing in the appearance of this animal," he wrote in *The Windward Road*, "is anything near as curious as its incredible sloth. I use the term in its original sense of 'slowness' —with none of its acquired connotation of *reprehensible* slowness. The sloth of these animals is one of the marvels of nature. It is a mockery of motion, an eerily mechanical, nerve-wracking slowness that contractile protoplasm was never meant to support. The cytoplasm of an amoeba streams faster than a sloth flees from a hungry boa constrictor. And besides being thus pointlessly, unbearably slow in everything it undertakes, the sloth is hesitant and vacillating in undertaking anything."

Sloths look like something that has survived out of the geological past, as indeed they have. Yet they are certainly successful in the modern world, being common almost everywhere in the rain forest of South America. Their very slowness may well be an adaptation for life in the trees, though no one has yet probed this aspect of the matter. On the other hand, it would seem to make them so defenseless as to be easy victims for any predator, though the two-toed sloth, if pressed, has been known to swipe viciously with its baling-hook foreleg. Perhaps their best defense is that they are extremely tough—sloths can survive mutilations that would kill almost any other vertebrate—and that their upside-down position makes it hard for animals like the big cats to get at them.

Being herbivores, sloths do not have to work hard for their food: leaves and fruit are always within easy reach. The three-toed was long thought to be almost exclusively dependent upon the *Cecropia* tree for its food, but it has recently been learned that its diet may vary widely.

Sloths are hard to see in the forest, not only because of their slow movements but also because their coarse, shaggy hair has a greenish hue in the rainy season. This is caused by another real curiosity of nature: microscopic green algae grow in the hair, which is distinctively grooved in each genus. According to William

Beebe, the grooves are longitudinal and quite pronounced in the two-toed, while they are transverse and less conspicuous in the three-toed, but the effect is the same, and this unusual example of symbiosis is still further enhanced by the presence of certain small moths which make their home in the algae and can often be seen crawling through the sloth's hair. The hair itself, because of the upside-down existence of its owner, grows in the opposite direction from that of other furry animals, i.e., from the belly toward the back.

The sloth's relatives, the South American anteaters, are very different-looking animals. There are three kinds: *Myrmecophaga*, the giant anteater; *Tamandua*, the lesser anteater; and the silky anteater, *Cyclopes*. All are equipped with powerful forelegs and claws for tearing open the nests of ants and termites, and all have long, sticky tongues for gathering up their prey.

The biggest of the three, the giant anteater, looks bigger than it really is. Discounting its head and tail, its body is about the size of a collie dog. The tail, however, is truly magnificent—long, bushy, fanning out almost like an ostrich plume from a central spine. With tail and pointed snout, the animal is six to seven feet in length, and in its gray fur with a characteristic black band running from its cheeks to its chest, it is strikingly handsome. The giant anteater sleeps with its tail curled over its head and shoulders in cooler weather, suggesting that a primary function of this fine appendage may be to provide warmth. Another idea is that it may serve as an umbrella during the rainy season, and still another that it may be used to swish away annoying insects.

The giant anteater is most often seen on the ground, although it can climb and, like the sloths, even swim when the occasion demands. Perhaps its most curious characteristic is its walk. The long, sharp, curved claws cannot retract, so the animal walks on the calloused sides of its paws with the claws curved inward. This way of walking may serve to keep the claws from becoming dulled or, conversely, it may simply be the result of the claws making normal walking difficult. Whatever the reason, it gives the anteater a peculiar and rather clumsy-looking gait. It is an inoffensive creature, but if attacked it can defend itself surprisingly well, standing up on its hind legs and swinging savagely with its clawed forefeet—as many dogs, and probably even some of the predatory cats, have occasionally learned to their pain.

WHILE the giant anteaters are largely inhabitants of the open savannas of northern South America, where they feed on termites in large nests, the lesser anteater has found its food in the forest. Fox-sized, with a head and body shaped much like that of its larger cousin, *Tamandua* differs most notably in its tail, which is prehensile and almost naked. Though the lesser anteater is more often seen on the ground, because it is more conspicuous there, it actually spends about half its time in the trees, and is a rapid and skillful climber. If cornered, it can fight as effectively as the giant species.

The silky anteater, finally, is a completely tree-adapted animal. A beautiful little creature about the size of a squirrel, with soft, golden-yellow fur and a prehensile tail, it is as arboreal as the sloths, with the same permanently hooked claws, and like them moves about the branches with great deliberation. Its slowness is probably partly due to poor eyesight. It subsists on tree-nesting termites and furthermore it is strictly nocturnal in its habits.

Members of the third group of the edentates have become adapted to a completely different way of life: they live entirely on the ground, never climbing above it but able to burrow down into it with extraordinary agility. These are

THE SLOTH'S POPULATED FUR

The shaggy coat of the brown two-toed sloth plays host to both a plant and an insect. The plant is a form of algae that grows in the grooves of the sloth's corrugated hairs (below, left), turning the animal greenish and camouflaging it against marauding eagles. The insect is a small moth (below, right). Although it has well-developed wings, it seldom flies; instead, it spends its time scuttling in and out of the fur. This association is beneficial to the moth because its larvae are believed to eat the alga, but what good —if any—it does the sloth is not known.

the armadillos—nine genera and perhaps 20 species. Unlike the anteaters the armadillos do have teeth, but they are all molars, peglike in shape and among the most primitive found in mammals. All of them are natives of the Neotropical realm except one, the nine-banded armadillo, which seems bent on extending its range ever farther northward, having in recent years traversed Texas and most of the southern United States. This little nomad is extraordinary in its reproduction—a normal birth always consists of quadruplets of the same sex.

Most of the armadillos live in Brazil, Bolivia and Argentina, and though they are popularly thought of as being animals of the world's more arid areas, they actually occupy a variety of habitats, from grassland to forest. Some are confined to one particular environment, some are at home in several. In size they range from the giant armadillo of the tropical forest, which weighs up to 100 pounds, to the tiny fairy armadillo of Bolivia and western Argentina, which is only some five inches long from snout to tip of tail. The fairy armadillo has long fur on its flanks which hangs down below its independent shell, and the young, during their early development, are hidden in this protective curtain.

THE most striking thing about an armadillo's appearance is, of course, its armor. Since this seems obviously to be a defensive adaptation, it is generally believed that armadillos, when attacked, make the best use of it by rolling themselves into a ball. One species does indeed do this—the three-banded armadillo of the Argentine pampas—but it is the only one. The others seek safety in burrowing, and the rapidity with which they can get down into loose or soft soil is astonishing. "The instant one was perceived," wrote Charles Darwin of the Argentine pichy, a relative of the nine-banded armadillo, "it was necessary in order to catch it, almost to tumble off one's horse; for if the soil was soft the animal burrowed so quickly, that its hinder quarters had almost disappeared before one could alight."

There is some evidence that armadillos are extremely sensitive to ground vibrations made by approaching animals which might attack them; certainly they are so quick to take alarm that by the time a searcher gets to where they are, there is often nothing to be seen but a small heap of dug-up earth. Their claws and limbs are very powerful, and if they elect to run, as they may if caught on hard or rocky ground, they are surprisingly fast. Though they may not look like desirable prey, they are; their meat is as tasty as that of a suckling pig, and they are as highly prized for it by humans as they are by more lowly predators. In cold weather, some armadillos are fond of sun bathing. They fall asleep on their backs while absorbing the sun's warmth and, like dogs, appear to have dreams punctuated by trembling and frequent convulsions. At such times, they are quite vulnerable. Armadillos appear to be generally omnivorous, although much of their life history still awaits further research. What, for instance, lies behind the differentiation in the number of bands which separate their tesselated plates of armor? These bands are handy to identify some species, ranging as they do from three to nine, but how and why they got that way from what may originally have been a solid shell is an intriguing question.

Certainly the armadillos, like the sloths, the anteaters and the marsupials, go all the way back to the original mammal population of South America, the rich fauna that developed during the continent's long period of isolation. During all that span of 70 million years, invaders were few and far between because not many animals are equipped to traverse the barriers of wide ocean spaces. However, there is evidence that a few managed to make the journey from time to time; there are types that do not belong to the original mammal population of South America and yet they were well established there before the continent was rejoined to North America. Obviously they drifted across during the interval between land bridges. This is the case with the monkeys, which were dealt with in the previous chapter, and with a few rodents, of which South America has some very characteristic forms.

Rodents clearly have been in South America for a long time, perhaps since as far back as the late Eocene, some 45 million years ago. They came by a similar process of island hopping that presumably populated parts of Australasia. The living South American rodents are classified today in 15 families, and of these, eight are found nowhere else in the world. It is difficult to write about them, because so few have well-known English names, while their Spanish names are apt to differ from country to country, or even from one part of a country to another. This leads easily to confusion as to just exactly what animal is being talked about, or whether intermediate types may exist between what appear to be distinct species. Often, too, little is known about their habits, for despite the fact that they may be very common animals, many live in such remote places that few scientists have been able to observe them. Certain among them, however, are well known, the most familiar being those commercial fur-bearers, the chinchillas and the nutrias, and the so-called guinea pigs, the agoutis, the pacas and the capybaras.

The most valuable of all the rodents are the chinchillas and nutrias, two whose fur is as soft as the finest known. One type of chinchilla, the mountain vizcacha, lives in the Andes at altitudes up to 16,000 feet, one of the highest ranges tolerated by any mammal anywhere. Unable to dig burrows like its relatives lower down, it inhabits crevices and small caves in the rock, sharing them communally and nibbling lichens for food. The larger plains vizcacha is a collector of all manner of junk, from ordinary stones and hardened cakes of dung to household articles, all of which it piles in disorderly fashion around the mouth of its burrow, for reasons unfathomable to man. The present commercial chinchillas were hunted so unmercifully for their fur from the beginning of the 19th Century that they almost became extinct, but in 1923 success was at last achieved in breeding captive animals in the United States. The water-dwelling nutrias, a South American equivalent of the muskrat, were also bred with great success in North America when the native populations began to dwindle. They became a serious pest in Louisiana and elsewhere after a few individuals escaped and began breeding and spreading in swampy areas.

Guinea pigs are neither pigs nor do they come from Guinea—they got their English name because they were first brought to England aboard ships called Guineamen, which traded goods and slaves between Guinea in Africa, the West Indies and South America, and England. The little rodents made interesting household pets and the name stuck. Technically, they belong to the genus *Cavia* and should be called cavies. They turned out to be extremely useful laboratory animals because they are susceptible to a number of human diseases and react in human fashion to experiments in disease prevention. In fact, their association with humans goes back a long way. The ancestors of the Incas, for example, domesticated them for food. They live in many different environments, from mountains through open country to tropical forests, and have developed a number of different species. Unfortunately, little is known about the wild forms, which are often nocturnal and shy, and are surprisingly difficult to keep in cap-

THE HIGH AND THE LOW

Though related, the two vizcachas shown here differ in appearance and behavior. The jack-rabbit-sized mountain vizcacha (above), one of the world's highest-dwelling mammals, is found on Andean slopes to an altitude of 16,000 feet. It lives in rock crevices, protected from the noonday sun and the intense cold of night. It feeds by day, bounding up slopes on its long hind legs. The bigger plains vizcacha (below) lives on the pampas. Unlike the mountain variety, it digs a burrow and comes out under cover of darkness.

tivity. I tried hard to domesticate one particular species which turned up quite frequently in traps around the laboratory where I worked in Colombia, but most of them promptly died—and it looked to me as though they died of fright. The only way I could keep any alive was to put them in a cage with some half-grown individuals of the domesticated species, but I never did get them to breed.

Agoutis, on the other hand, domesticate easily, and it is a wonder that no serious efforts to do so have ever been made. They are the size of a rabbit, and their meat is even tastier. Furthermore, they are common from Argentina to Mexico on the forest floors, where they dig large burrows around the roots of trees. They are odd-looking animals, having a short head attached to a stocky body with surprisingly slender legs. These legs have two prime attributes: they have remarkably large claws for digging and they can carry an alarmed agouti back to its burrow with amazing speed.

Agoutis have no particular food-getting problem; they feed mostly on plants and insects. Where people abound, they have sensibly taken up a nocturnal life. Elsewhere, however, in places like Barro Colorado Island, where they have never been hunted, they can be seen at almost any time of day. And they are interesting to watch: socially, for example, they are rather quixotic animals, often fighting among themselves so fiercely that individuals may be deliberately trampled to death, while at other times they may be seen feeding together peacefully in fairly large groups.

Pacas are larger relatives of the agoutis—and, incidentally, make even better eating—and capybaras are the largest rodents anywhere, which is their principal claim to fame. They look like nightmarishly large guinea pigs, which is what they really are, attaining lengths of up to four feet and weights of 160 pounds. Long ago, in the Pliocene, they had an even larger relative, *Phoberomys*, which was the size of a rhinoceros. Today, their role in South American life is more comparable to that of the African hippopotamus: they feed mostly on land but use the water as a refuge. They are excellent swimmers and divers, and can remain submerged for as long as eight or 10 minutes at a time.

CURIOSITIES abound among other members of the rodent family south of the border. There is a spiny rat whose fur consists of soft, flat, sharp-pointed spines and bristles. There is the tuco-tuco, an ecological equivalent of North America's pocket gopher. It gets its name from its odd, subterranean call, which comes up eerily from the underground galleries dug by these little creatures. They live on the plains where the din they set up below ground has been described as sounding like "the hammers of the Nibelungen." There are also porcupines which can swing by their tails. These are gentle and nocturnal in their habits and not as formidably armed with quills as the North American types. Curiously, there are only three genera of squirrels, all of them tree dwellers, but scarcely noticeable in the forests. Part of the squirrel niche, it would seem, was long ago preempted by marmosas, monkeys and marmosets, who evolved better adaptations to the variegated opportunities offered by life in the burgeoning tropical forests.

That, of course, is what determines who survives and who does not over the long, slow, endlessly changing course of life through geologic time. The animals we know today, in many cases, are marching toward the same oblivion as those who marched before them long ago. To the paleontologist, this is the story whose fascination never dims: to rebuild the past from the remains—fossil, bone or living creature—that have survived into the present.

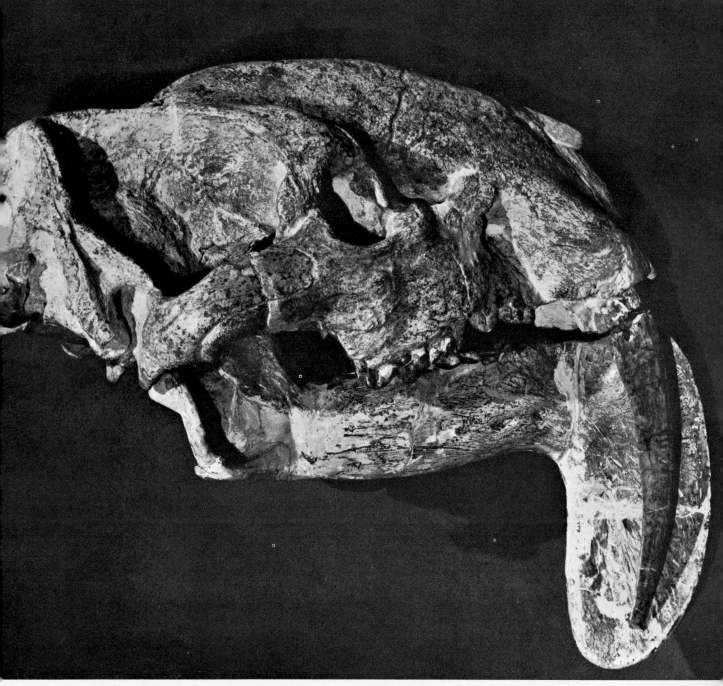

THYLACOSMILUS, A LEOPARD-SIZED MARSUPIAL WITH SIX-INCH TEETH, LEFT THIS FOSSIL SKULL. IT BECAME EXTINCT 10 MILLION YEARS AGO

The Oldtime Mammals

During the eons that South America remained an island continent, a unique community of mammals developed there undisturbed, all radiating from a few ancient orders. But with the rising of the isthmus at Panama during the Pliocene, competitors poured south. Some oldtimers, like the opossum, survived the challenge, but most, like the saber-toothed marsupial above, are now extinct.

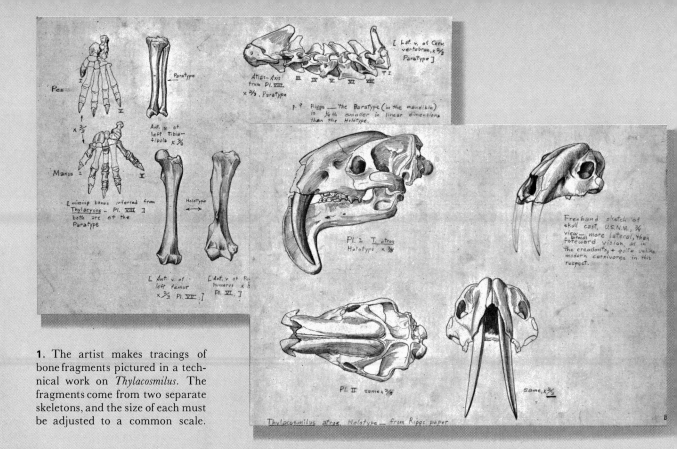

1. The artist makes tracings of bone fragments pictured in a technical work on *Thylacosmilus*. The fragments come from two separate skeletons, and the size of each must be adjusted to a common scale.

How an Artist Re-creates the Past

A STUDY FOR THE HEAD of *Thylacosmilus* shows the extensions of the lower jaw, against which its two great fangs fitted, as in an open sheath.

A paleontologist works like a detective. His clues are fossils, and the ingenuity he uses to weave these and related shreds of evidence into a fully articulated picture of life as it existed millions of years ago would have awed Sherlock Holmes.

In 1926, Dr. Elmer S. Riggs of the Chicago Field Museum of Natural History unearthed in northwestern Argentina pieces of a fossil skull (photographed on the previous page) as well as a few other bones of a creature which bore an extraordinary likeness to a carnivorous saber-toothed tiger but was unmistakably a marsupial dating from the Pliocene. He named his discovery *Thylacosmilus*. How a complete animal is reconstructed step by step from such fragments is shown in these drawings made by Jay Matternes, a specialist in this work.

3. Last step in bringing *T̵̵smilus* to life is for the artist t̵ a series of sketches based knowledge of animals in gen̵ he tries to work out how an a of this type would probably

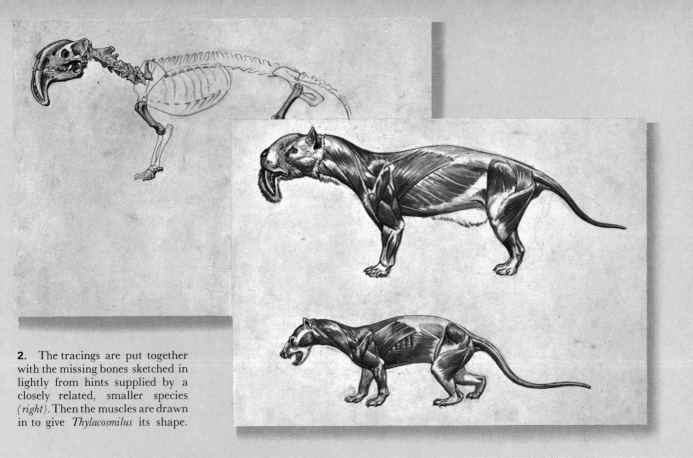

2. The tracings are put together with the missing bones sketched in lightly from hints supplied by a closely related, smaller species *(right)*. Then the muscles are drawn in to give *Thylacosmilus* its shape.

more
dog-like

Possibly, greater slope
to back; more nearly
plantigrade hind
feet (See Scott
1937, p. 705)

[See the photo of
Chicago specimen, neg.
573 - approx. gape of
jaws]

Stabbing
Action

The Megatherium Brought to Life

An artist's final step in re-creating an extinct animal is to depict it as it probably appeared in its natural surroundings. This is what Jay Matternes has done here with a giant ground sloth, *Megatherium*. His job was easier than with *Thylacosmilus* because he had a complete skeleton to start with. But he still had the difficult task of determining the color and nature of his subject's fur. The result derives partly from a study of the fur of living arboreal sloths and partly from the extraordinary fact that a piece of skin from a closely related extinct ground sloth was found at a ranch in Chile some years ago. This gave Matternes the clues he needed as to texture and enabled him to color the animal reddish blond.

THE FULL SKELETON OF A MEGATHERIUM IS OVER 15 FEET LONG

THE MUSCULAR OVERLAY emphasizes the massiveness of *Megatherium's* hind legs and tail, which form a tripod stout enough to support its five-ton weight. This helps the artist visualize the posture in which *Megatherium* fed. A puzzle is the single huge claw on each of the hind feet; these may have been used as the African elephant uses his tusks, to uproot small trees.

A COMPLETE RECONSTRUCTION embodies what is known about the ground sloth. For example, the teeth are obviously those of a vegetarian, and the troughlike shape of the lower jaw indicates a long, flexible tongue. The huge carapace of the glyptodont, in the foreground, many of which have been found, makes reconstruction of that armored animal relatively simple.

63

A Water Hole on the Pampas
One Million Years Ago

During his famous voyage, Darwin unearthed the partial remains of the two extinct ungulates shown in this reconstruction. He theorized that *Macrauchenia* (the large, loose-jointed creature on the left) was a forerunner of the guanaco, and a colleague speculated that *Toxodon* (right), of which Darwin had brought back only a skull, was an early rodent. Both were wrong. Much evidence has been gathered since Darwin's day, and we now know that none of the great variety of ungulates

that developed in South America prior to the land bridge at Panama has any living descendant, though these two species did survive well into the Pleistocene.

The nasal openings in the skull of *Macrauchenia* indicate the presence of a proboscis in the living animal. In the reconstruction, *Macrauchenia* is pictured holding its nose clear of the water while drinking, showing that the artist did not think it was used for snuffing up water and squirting it into its mouth as

an elephant does. Rather, it is thought that the animal used its elongated nose to reach the tops of small trees, whose leaves formed one of the principal parts of its diet.

As for *Toxodon*, the placement of the ears high up on the skull is similar to that of the hippopotamus. This, with other clues, has led experts to list *Toxodon* as semiaquatic. The artist, taking that lead, has pictured it without hair, like the hippopotamus, though some other versions give it body hair.

JAWS AGAPE, a four-eyed opossum, named for the white spots over its eyes, flashes a set of sharp teeth. Noted for its fierce unopossumlike manner, this rat-sized marsupial is arboreal.

The Persistent Opossums

Although most of the early marsupials that flourished in isolation in South America have succumbed to competition from placentals from the north, one family—the opossums—is still thriving. The best known of these is the tough, adaptable common opossum, which, far from dying out, has penetrated widely into North America. Less familiar are its 10 cousins which live in the tropical American rain forests. These, like the woolly opossum, the four-eyed opossum and the little marmosa, nest and live for the most part up in trees, where they hunt insects and eat fruit. All these are much more handsome than the common species—and they also differ in character. They are often aggressive. To "play possum" by their rules is not to roll over and play dead but rather to show a ready will to defend oneself, albeit on a Lilliputian scale, from such natural enemies as owls, snakes and other larger predators.

66

EYE TO EYE, a tiny marmosa and a large tropical grasshopper stare at one another intently. Just what the grasshopper sees in the marmosa is uncertain; however, there is little doubt as

to what the marmosa sees in the grasshopper—dinner. This rarely seen "mouse opossum," an inhabitant of the upper levels of the rain forests, is no bigger than a man's thumb. Like all opossums, it has a bare, prehensile tail. Its fur, on the other hand, is nearly as silky as that of a chinchilla, and it keeps it spotlessly clean by constant combing with claws and teeth.

Sloths: Survival through Slowness

The three-toed sloth shown here, and its cousin the two-toed—along with anteaters and armadillos—comprise the order Edentata and trace their lineage back to the very earliest South American mammals. It seems strange that the sloth, among the stupidest and certainly the slowest of all living mammals, should be the sole living heir to the great *Megatherium*. Interestingly, its very torpor, both external and internal, is what has preserved it. Its life is spent hanging apparently motionless from a branch. It does move, but so slowly as to escape the eyes of predators; it may take 30 seconds to shift a leg a few inches, and its all-out speed in rushing to an endangered infant was once clocked at 14 feet a minute. A sloth never makes an unnecessary gesture. It never cleans itself, but instead exploits as camouflage the green algae that grow in its fur. It even sneezes slowly, and its bowels are so regulated that it can go a week without evacuating while waiting for the concealing sound of rain.

CRADLING HER YOUNG, a mother three-toed sloth clings to a branch. A sloth's limbs are so well adapted to this use that it can hang indefinitely—with less effort than most other animals use to stand upright.

69

Anteaters: A Unique Appetite

Though anteating mammals like Australia's spiny "echidna" and the African pangolin do exist in other parts of the world, the three South American genera pictured here are considered to be the only "true" anteaters. They are also the only "true" members of the edentate order, as they have no teeth at all, while their cousins the sloths and armadillos do.

Anteater genealogy is something of a mystery; no fossils of earlier forms have ever been found. And yet it is certain that these highly specialized animals have been a long time developing. All three genera have spoutlike snouts, excellent for poking into rotten logs and anthills. Their tongues are even longer and covered with an extremely sticky saliva that picks up anything it touches: dirt, wood particles, termites—and also ants. The latter, having very hard shells, pose something of a digestion problem. Anteaters solve it with powerful stomach muscles which grind the ants much as a bird's gizzard grinds corn.

A TAMANDUA, or three-toed anteater, thrusts its snout into a hanging termite nest. Its prehensile tail, so different from the giant anteater's, indicates a long history of arboreal living.

A GIANT ANTEATER strides across its range, the open savannalands from Costa Rica south to Argentina. From the point of its tubelike head to the tip of its long-haired tail, it may measure seven feet and weigh upward of 100 pounds. A daytime feeder, its claws hack open stone-hard termite mounds and it may consume as many as 30,000 termites or ants a day.

A SILKY ANTEATER, so called for its soft fur, is no bigger than a squirrel, and in comparison with the giant anteater's, its nose is a mere nub. But it manages well enough in its quest for ants and termites, which it pursues in the trees of rain forests from Mexico to Paraguay. Like the tamandua, it is nocturnal and strictly arboreal. Its prehensile tail makes it a deft climber.

71

Armadillos: A Durable Design

The third family of edentates is the armadillos, unique in being the only living mammals to have shells. These are not solid like a turtle's, but are actually groups of large scales joined together into bony sections: the "bands" that give the various species their names—three-banded, nine-banded, etc. The bands fit together like pieces of armor to provide both protection and flexibility. The latter is probably the more important asset to the armadillo, since it enables the animal to move quickly and to dig fast—and digging is its chief method of escape from predators. By contrast, the armadillo's ancient cousin, the glyptodont, long extinct, probably had to rely entirely on armor for protection, since it had a solid, high-domed, completely inflexible shell.

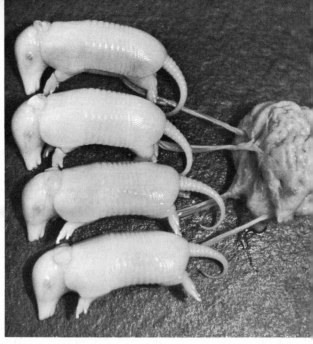

FOUR EMBRYOS attached to a common placenta illustrate an extraordinary and invariable rule: the nine-banded armadillo always gives birth to quadruplets, either all male or all female.

SMALLEST OF THE TRIBE, a fairy armadillo has a loose shell which is connected to its five-inch body only along the spine, partially covering a dense coat of white hair.

BIGGEST MEMBER, the giant armadillo, here shares a zoo meal with a medium-sized, six-banded variety. The giant is about five feet long and may weigh up to 100 pounds.

A NINE-BANDED ARMADILLO roots among earthworms on the forest floor. Because of their bony shells, armadillos are heavier than water—the specific gravity of the one shown above is 1.06 —and ought to sink. But like all edentates they live in a land of river and flood, and must be able to swim. They manage it by an unusual ability to inflate their intestines by gulping air.

THE PATAGONIAN CAVY, though no relation, looks something like an oversize European hare on stilts. Its long ears, bounding gait and fondness for grass all contribute to the likeness.

THE WORLD'S LARGEST RODENT is the capybara, which resembles a hog-sized, blunt-nosed muskrat. It has webbed feet for swimming and for walking over soft, swampy ground.

THE PACA, easily identified by the rows of white spots along its flanks, is nocturnal and vegetarian. It can live in various habitats, but prefers to make its burrow near water in the forest.

Rodents: Early Immigrants

Although it has its share of ordinary-looking mice and rats, South America is remarkable for a number of very large rodents found nowhere else. These are not as old as certain other oldtimers, like the marsupials, nor as newly arrived as some of the invaders who walked over the land bridge from the north. Instead, they are in-between arrivals, island-hoppers like the monkeys, who put in an appearance during the Eocene some 50 million years ago when South America was still isolated.

Like all rodents, South America's representatives are varied and extremely numerous. Many of them look like the common concept of a rodent, with the pointed "rat" faces familiar all over the world; but others are distinguished by big blunt heads, long bodies and usually short stumpy tails. Some of them have surprisingly long legs—which make them look more like small ruminants than rodents.

THE PERUVIAN CAVY is a domesticated version of the guinea pig. Cavies are clean little animals, gentle and affectionate, and were first kept by the Incas' ancestors.

A PACARANA, so named for its likeness to the paca, gets a bite of dinner. Like other large South American rodents, this animal is hunted for its flesh by natives.

4

Talented
Newcomers

No one knows how long South America was isolated from the rest of the world, but however long it may have been—possibly 60 million years—it included a period of particular significance: the rise of the mammals to pre-eminence in the animal world. On the isolated continent, as we now have seen, these developed along peculiar lines, not only among the marsupials but also among the placentals. Elsewhere, on the major land mass of the world—in North America, Eurasia and Africa—others were evolving which would eventually win out in the struggle for survival. And when the land bridges between South America and the world continent rose out of the sea again in the Pliocene and the invaders from the north marched in, the curious creatures which had flourished on the southern continent proved no match for them. Survivors of long competition, the newcomers soon made themselves at home in most niches of the various continental habitats, adapting themselves in various ways.

The explosive development of one family of newcomers well illustrates this drama of competition and survival. In the Upper Pliocene a group of rodents, the cricetines, came to South America and began to establish themselves. These were members of what we know as the hamster family—small creatures well adapted for a generally herbivorous life on the ground. All of the Old World members of this family today are pastoral in their habits—country mice in the true sense of the word, grazing and/or browsing in forest and field. In South America, however, there were many other new opportunities, and as a consequence the cricetine rodents developed in all sorts of astonishing ways.

In the relatively short time they have been there—at the most three million years—they have burst forth into at least 50 genera exclusive to the Neotropical alone, filling numerous niches with entirely new adaptations. So distinctive did these little animals become that they have assumed, with the Central and North American species, the status of a tribe within their own family: the New World mice. In South America, they range from the swampy lowlands of the Amazon to the highest altitude that can sustain mammalian life in the Andes, from the equator south to the frigid barrens bordering the Strait of Magellan. Far from being mere grazers and browsers, the New World mice today include house dwellers, tree climbers, marsh dwellers, diggers, swimmers, jumpers, and even some species that eat fish. In short, the cricetine rodents provide a classic example of adaptive radiation on a huge scale.

The tree-dwelling species, for example, include the climbing rats and mice, which nest, feed and breed in trees, coming down only occasionally for food and water. All of these have evolved paws particularly adapted to climbing, with sharp claws to grip the bark; they also have long, tufted tails which serve as balancing tools. The marsh rats, by contrast, have developed partially webbed feet, and many of them even have claws on the thumbs of their forefeet to help them dig burrows in the banks of streams. The digging adaptations are carried to even greater extremes in certain molelike mice which exploit the opportunities of life underground and have powerful digging claws and long, pointed noses. By contrast, the jumping species have developed the spade-shaped hind feet and thick, strong, kangaroolike thighs characteristic of jumpers the world over. Some of the New World mice make the best of several environments, nesting on the ground but foraging in the trees or going to the water of streams and lakes for their food. The earliest arrivals appear to have taken up life in the forest, and some of these now appear to be radiating toward life in the open. On the other hand, some of the field dwellers seem to be heading in the opposite direction, toward life in the woods. Clearly, in the South American forms, the process of adaptive radiation in many cases is still in flux—as the mammalogist Philip Hershkovitz puts it, radiation "is still so much in progress that it is not uncommon to find ancestral stocks living contemporaneously with their specialized or progressive descendants."

As impressive as the cricetine rodents were in adapting themselves to the opportunities afforded by life in South America, it has always seemed to me that the masters of the tropical forest environment in the southern continent are those clever members of the raccoon family, the coatis, or coatimundis. These are descendants of late- and post-Pliocene invaders, although some South American members of this family mysteriously made their way down from North America as early as the Miocene. These early island hoppers, however, did not survive into modern times. We know them today only as fossils.

The family itself, the Procyonidae, is a curiously diverse group of carnivores, omnivores and frugivores. Except for the lesser panda of Southeast Asia, the family is entirely American. The raccoons are among its most familiar members; others are the ring-tailed "cat," or cacomistle, of the southwestern United

States, and the coatis, kinkajous and olingos of Central and South America.

Coatis are the size of raccoons and have many of the raccoon's habits—but they have longer and much more expressive tails and an elongated, very flexible and mobile snout. Coatis' noses are extremely sensitive organs which get poked into every sort of forest situation as the animals sniff their way through life. The females and young travel in bands of as few as eight or as many as 20, but the males, for the most part, lead solitary lives. Though they live on the ground, coatis are excellent climbers. They are fearless, aggressive animals, and their sharp claws and cooperative behavior make them formidable opponents for other forest animals. A pack of coatis is perfectly capable of killing a dog that ventures to attack, a fact of which many a hunter in South America has on occasion been painfully aware.

Raccoons are known to be intelligent, but coatis, to my mind, are even brighter. Like raccoons, they are omnivorous, eating nuts and fruits as well as any small animal they can catch or dig out of a hiding place. They are often kept as pets, and they are very charming when small, with an engaging capacity for getting into all kinds of mischief. But as they become adult, they tend to wander away in the mating season. They usually come back afterward, the males often with the marks of fierce combat on them, but adult coatis on the whole are difficult to discipline, apparently feeling quite reasonably that if they are swatted for some breach of human rules, they have a right to bite back.

ONCE had a most unusual opportunity to observe coati intelligence at first-hand on the island of Barro Colorado, where I spent several months with the illustrious ornithologist Frank Chapman. Although he was dedicated primarily to the study of bird habits, everything in his environment was of interest to Chapman, and he had become quite friendly with some of the solitary male coatis that roamed near the laboratory clearing. However, one thing about the coatis annoyed him: they regularly stole the bananas he put out as bait for the toucans he was studying. He decided to rig a coati-proof feeding station for the birds. He strung a wire between the porch of his cottage and a neighboring tree to serve as a trolley for a cigar box which could be baited with bananas and pulled with a second wire out into the open to attract the birds.

It was a fine idea, but it turned out not to be coati-proof. The very first day it was put into use, a coati came out into the clearing, sniffed the redolent banana atmosphere, and in a surprisingly short time, by sniffing from various places like a surveyor making a triangular observation, located the fruit in the cigar box. Up the tree he went, and out onto the wire. His tightrope act was nerve-tingling to watch, but he got the banana. With this, Chapman decided for the time being to abandon birds and take up the study of coatis.

The next step, as I recall it, was to hang the banana under the cigar box at the end of a three-foot string. The coati, which by this time had become an amazingly skillful high-wire performer, solved this with no difficulty—he simply pulled up the banana, hand over hand, and ate it. Next the banana was hung from the end of a nine-foot pole which projected from the ground to a point just under the cigar box—the coati made one futile trip along the wire out to the box to discover this was not the way to get at the fruit, and then figured out the right way and climbed the pole. He even learned to get the banana when it was hung from a string which had been thrown over the wire, with the other end anchored on the ground: at first he simply pulled on the string, and when he was unable to pull the banana over the wire, bit through the string so that the bait fell down. No matter what Chapman did, the coati eventually got his fruit. His behavior was so unusually "intelligent" that, after this experience, I would be willing to back the coati in any I.Q. test against any American mammal except the *Cebus* monkey.

Incidentally, these tests, apart from demonstrating the coatis' ingenuity and ability to learn, also proved the supreme importance of their noses to coatis. Chapman carved and painted a beautifully realistic banana and tried this out as bait in various ways. If the fake banana was hung out alone, no attention was paid to it at all. If other bananas were hung nearby, the coati unfailingly could tell the fake one from a distance of six to eight inches.

COATIS as a rule do not display any great affinity for water, finding all their food on dry land, but they have a close relative, *Procyon cancrivorus*, which is actually a semiaquatic raccoon. Its specific name means "crab-eater"—and indeed it does eat crabs, shrimps and frogs which it catches in the rivers along whose banks it lives. The crab-eating raccoon is in almost all respects similar to our North American raccoon. It is nocturnal and if it does not find the food it seeks in the water, it will eat small birds, insects and fruits and will gnaw sugar cane and green shoots in gardens. Its tail is ringed and still quite bushy, though it has shorter fur and longer legs than its North American cousin.

The oddest member of the South American raccoon family is certainly the kinkajou, which is usually known locally as a monkey. It does have a monkey-like look about it, even to having a prehensile tail (along with the binturong of southern Asia, it is the only carnivore so equipped). Some early naturalists even thought kinkajous should be classified as lemurs, but there is now general agreement that the raccoon family is where they belong. With their prehensile tails and climbing paws, kinkajous are extremely adept at getting about in the trees, and though fruits are their preferred diet, they will really eat anything, including insects. Kinkajous are sometimes kept as pets, but the fact that they are nocturnal creatures is rather an inconvenience in most households. In pet shops they are often called "honey bears," partly because of a fondness for honey and partly because they have honey-colored fur.

Very similar to the kinkajous but much more rarely seen are the olingos. They, too, are highly adapted to life in the trees, but without prehensile tails, theirs being merely bushy and handsome balancing organs. Olingos eat the same things as kinkajous and often feed with them, which is confusing to observers. Like kinkajous, they are nocturnal, but they are much more shy and they are seldom seen in captivity.

Among other carnivores, South America also has its share of members of the cat, dog, weasel and bear families. All of these are unquestionably newcomers to the continent which joined in the march across the isthmus once the land bridge was re-established in the Pliocene.

The largest of the American cats are the jaguars and the pumas. The most obvious difference between the two is in their coats: jaguars are spotted, somewhat like the Old World leopards, although the spots are larger, while pumas are uniformly colored, from pale gray to sandy brown, depending on where they live, with a spot of white at the chin. As usual, this is a result of adaptation: the spotted jaguars are basically tropical animals, seldom seen north of Mexico, which prefer forest living, near rivers and estuaries. By comparison to pumas, this is a relatively narrow range. Pumas live not only in forests but in savanna country and in the mountains—they are an excellent example of an animal that ranges through several subregions, being found all the way from Argentina to Canada. Thus they are not as narrowly specialized for a particular habitat as the jaguar, either in coloration or in other ways.

Jaguars will pursue almost any kind of animal prey, but they are particularly fond of river reptiles, including even caimans, South America's versions of the alligator. They catch the caimans ashore, leap on their backs and kill them by breaking their necks. They are also very skillful fishermen, swatting fish out of the water with a swift stroke of the paw. Unlike most cats, they actually seem to enjoy swimming and have even been known to swim from the seashore to offshore islands. In the forest, pumas will take much the same kind of prey in the same way, but elsewhere, in open country and in the mountains, they pursue sheep, goats, deer and even the larger hoofed animals like horses and cows.

More distinctive and interesting than the South American cats are the members of the dog family, the Neotropical canines. Curiously enough, there are on the continent no wild species of *Canis*, the genus which includes such familiar creatures as wolves, coyotes and the domesticated dog. Some South American Indians, including the Incas of Peru, had domesticated dogs in pre-European times, and of course dogs were brought over by settlers from Spain and Portugal, but none of these have escaped to establish themselves in the wild.

A canine genus that is represented in South America—and amply so—is a peculiar one, known as *Dusicyon*, that occurs only there. As far as local people are concerned, this genus supplies a full roster of wolves, foxes, dogs and jackals, although to the scientific eye these are all quite different from such creatures. The differences are marked in some cases, but these animals are playing the same ecological role as the true wolves, foxes and other canines elsewhere.

Thus, for example, there is a somewhat wolflike species in the bleak forests of Tierra del Fuego and southern Chile, a running animal which ranges far for its prey of rodents, birds and lambs. Another wolf type once inhabited the Falkland Islands but was exterminated by sheep farmers: this creature was so tame that it would lick the hands of its killers. How the ancestor of this form ever reached the islands remains a fascinating zoogeographical mystery. The currents are adverse and the distance too great for a swimming animal, and though a *Dusicyon* might have been domesticated by the Patagonian Indians, there is no evidence that these Indians ever reached the islands to bring a dog with them.

THE pampas "fox," *Dusicyon gymnocercus* of the Argentine, is a solitary hunter that often lives in the abandoned burrows of the vizcachas. Curiously, it has also adopted the vizcacha habit of collecting things, and bits of rope and other odds and ends are often found in its lairs. Another *Dusicyon* living in forests along the banks of rivers subsists, in addition to a normal fox diet, on crabs, crayfish and shrimps, for which it dives like any otter.

Some of the various kinds of *Dusicyon* have been caught only rarely, and little is known about their habits. This is true, for instance, of *Dusicyon fulvipes*, a species discovered on a Chilean island by Charles Darwin in the course of the famous voyage of the *Beagle*. Darwin described the capture of this first specimen thus: "In the evening we reached the island of San Pedro, where we found the *Beagle* at anchor. In doubling the point, two of the officers landed to take a round of angles with the theodolite. A fox of a kind said to be peculiar to the island, and very rare in it, and which is a new species, was sitting on the rocks. He was so intently absorbed in watching the work of the officers, that I was able, by quietly walking up behind, to knock him on the head with my geological hammer. This fox, more curious or more scientific, but less wise, than the generality of his brethren, is now mounted in the museum of the Zoological Society." No other specimens were captured for nearly a hundred years, and the species was thought to be extinct. Then, in 1922, two more specimens were trapped by an expedition from Chicago's Field Museum.

Another of the peculiar South American canines, the maned wolf, is put in a different genus, *Chrysocyon*, by zoologists. More a fox than a wolf, this creature is solitary and shy, ranging the savannas of Brazil's Mato Grosso and the Chaco right up to the fringes of the rain forest. It also lives on the central plateau to heights of 3,000 feet. An omnivorous feeder, it subsists on certain fruits (Brazilians have named one *fruta de lobo*, or "wolf's fruit"), birds and small mammals. The maned wolf is an extremely fast runner, loping in an ungainly fashion on long, slender legs that give it the appearance of a fox on stilts. Its "mane" is a distinctive mass of fur around the neck, somewhat darker in color than its reddish coat.

PERHAPS the strangest of all South American canines, however, is the bush dog, *Icticyon* (now known as *Speothos*), whose closest relatives are the dhole of Asia and the Cape hunting dog of Africa. Like these, it is the last survivor of a very ancient subfamily and is only distantly related to other living canines. Bush dogs occur from Panama south to Brazil and have been reported mostly as living in relatively open country, with savannas and forests interspersed. There are few specimens in museums and even fewer in zoos, and little is known about their habits in the wild. It seems, however, that they hunt in packs of a dozen or so individuals, by contrast to the more solitary pampas fox and maned wolf. Short-legged and long-bodied, with a snub nose and short tail, the bush dog stands about a foot high at the shoulder. Pacas, the ecological equivalents of rabbits, are its favorite prey.

We had the good fortune to keep a bush dog alive at the Villavicencio laboratory for several months. It was brought to us by a countrywoman who had raised it from infancy, allowing it to run freely about her "rancho" and in general treating it as she would a dog. Certainly it was very doglike in its actions, and seemed to be as well adapted to life with man as any true dog. The bush dog, which we nicknamed Icty, always greeted those of us who played with her with piercing cries and excited tail-wagging. She loved to have her ears "scruffled" and would roll over on her back for a bellyrub, nipping our shoes or pulling our trouser leg if our attention lagged. Her cry at such times could only be

A CHASE IN THE AMAZON

Along the border of tropical forest and grassland in the upper Amazon, small stubby-legged bush dogs hunt rodents at dawn and dusk. Here they are pursuing a paca that has ventured out of the brush. Alerted to danger, the swift-running paca sprints off on its long legs. Like many other South American rodents, it often takes to the water to escape from enemies. But the dogs are good swimmers, too, and have learned to anticipate this tactic. Hunting in a pack, some individuals drive the animal toward the riverbank while another bush dog paddles along the shore and waits in ambush.

called a squeal—a continuous series of short, very high-pitched notes that she kept up as long as she was played with and that became in the end positively deafening. She would worry a stick or a handkerchief that was held out to her in much the same way that a terrier does. She would also retrieve sticks or other objects that were thrown, and seemed to take particular delight in retrieving things from the water of a small pool near the laboratory. She spent a great deal of time in this pool and could dive and swim under water with great facility. She obviously regarded herself as a "dog" and greeted our real dogs with great friendliness. I never dared allow her to play with other dogs, however: our terrier obviously thought Icty was some sort of cat, and I was afraid of the consequences of misunderstanding. Icty regarded any animal except man or dog as possible food, and I did not want her to change her mind about dogs.

These bush dogs are apparently truly rare everywhere. We always showed our Icty to visitors, hoping to get more specimens, but most of the local people had never heard of such a wild dog. I would think, judging from the behavior of this one captive individual, that the species could be easily domesticated—and that the animals could learn the whole bag of dog tricks. But apparently no attempt at domestication has ever succeeded.

The mustelids—weasels, skunks, otters and the like—are well represented among the newcomers on the South American continent, but for the most part they are not strikingly different from their relatives on other continents. The one exception is the largest of all the otters that live in the Amazon river system —the giant *Pteronura*, which grows to be as much as seven feet long. Like any other otter, this huge creature is playful and easily tamed. It preys on small mammals and aquatic birds, but unlike other river otters, it is a diurnal animal that lives and fishes in groups.

There is only one species of bear in South America, and that is the rare spectacled bear of the Andes. This animal, which gets its name from the yellow rings around its eyes, lives in the cloud forest at elevations of 8,000 or 9,000 feet. It is particularly fond of palm fruits—and it has the habit, odd for bears, of constructing a nest of branches and leaves.

This, then, is the order of the carnivores in South America, and all of them are clearly newcomers in the sense that they only became established after the Panama land bridge made the continent accessible on foot. The hoofed animals, the ungulates, are also newcomers—and they, too, are survivors of a dramatic competitive struggle. For they have now completely replaced the ancient grazing animals of the continent—the litopterns, notoungulates and other strange

creatures which we know today only as fossils. But newcomers though they are, some of these hoofed creatures now seem characteristically Neotropical.

This is true, for example, of the largest of the South American animals, the browsing tapirs. They are newcomers, though they look like anachronistic survivors from the geological past, with stout bodies, long and flexible snouts, and dainty hoofs on slender legs. Their past was actually on the world continent, not in South America: they are living members of an ancient order to which horses and rhinoceroses belong. Fossil tapirs dating as far back as the upper Eocene have been found in Europe, Asia and North America, and they were still a flourishing group when the Pliocene land bridge to the southern continent was formed. But only four species have survived into modern times—three in the Neotropical and one in Southeast Asia.

The three New World species are Baird's tapir, of Central America; the somewhat smaller Brazilian tapir, the most common species, which ranges over much of South America; and a slender, long-legged, woolly species with a particularly long snout that lives up to 15,000 feet high in the Andes.

TAPIRS are interesting creatures in many ways. Even in high mountains, they live always near streams, lakes or ponds—like hippopotamuses, they live off the land but spend a great deal of time in the water, and when they are alarmed, they take to the water as fast as they can go. In the forests, they have certain escape runs down which they plunge blindly, a habit which has given them an undeserved reputation for nearsightedness, since they blunder into anything that may be in the way, including, in one documented instance, an explorer's canoe which was beached on an Amazon tributary. The fact is that the tapirs invariably use their tunnels through the foliage, as a matter of habit. They will even run for a tunnel with a jaguar on their backs, and not infrequently this maneuver dislodges or even seriously injures their attacker, who finds himself scraped off by low branches. The tapirs, having very tough hides, may survive such an attack with no lasting damage.

Adding to their peculiar appearance, tapirs tend to be bare behind because they often sit down and slide down a riverbank or hill. They are also expert climbers in the mountains and surprisingly swift runners in open country. Their meat is tasty to humans as well as jaguars, which are their principal enemies.

Just as curious as the history and distribution of the tapirs is the story of the South American members of the camel family. We tend today to think of camels as beasts of Africa; actually, they originated in North America way back in the Eocene and spread from there to other parts of the world. There are four species in South America today—the guanacos, which live in herds from Patagonia to the high Andes, and the llamas, vicuñas and alpacas, all characteristic of the higher plateaus and mountain regions.

Of these four species, only the guanaco and vicuña are still wild. Like the camels in Asia and Africa, the llamas and alpacas have long since been domesticated. The larger of the two, the llama, which averages around 200 pounds in weight, was maintained originally as a source of meat and a beast of burden. The alpacas, on the other hand, serve as the Andean equivalent of sheep—they are raised primarily for wool and meat.

Every visitor to Patagonia comments on the guanaco herds—but the impressions are by no means uniform. Charles Darwin thought it "an elegant animal in a state of nature, with a long slender neck and fine legs" and considered it to be graceful in movement. But the paleontologist George Gaylord Simpson described it thus: "A guanaco looks like a small, humpless camel, which it is, and it also looks like a careless mixture of parts intended for other beasts and turned down as below standard, or like the result of a long period of miscegenation. It has a head something like that of a hornless deer, long ears like a mule, a neck that tries but fails to reach the giraffe standard, a scrawny, shapeless body, and gangling legs like those of a young colt."

In one respect, the vicuña is the most interesting of the four because it is strictly a high-altitude animal. From 12,000 feet on up, it lives as high as forage can be found. The thin, dry air of these great heights makes for rapid temperature changes: bodies absorb heat rapidly from solar radiation but lose it quickly when the sun's rays are blocked or when night falls. The thick fleece of high-mountain animals like the vicuña is the answer to this problem. Lungs, too, must greatly increase their capacity to absorb oxygen, for at high altitudes there is little enough of it—at 18,000 feet, for example, the lungs must take in twice as much air as at sea level to get the same amount of oxygen.

A few kinds of mammals seem to be able to move freely from lowlands to very considerable heights. One of these is the Andean deer of Chile and Argentina, which in summer months will range as high into the mountains as any pasturage can be found, but retreats to the lowlands with the coming of the winter snow.

Deer, in fact, have evolved in South America into a number of different types, occupying many of the niches elsewhere filled by goats (wild goats, for some reason, did not reach South America at all). The smallest deer in the world are the pudus, forest animals which live at high altitudes in Ecuador and Peru, ranging south to temperate forests at the tip of Chile. The various species are all about the size of terriers, with thick coats, sturdy hoofed legs and tiny spikelike antlers. At the other extreme of size is the marsh deer, which is about as big as a North American deer and inhabits marshy woodlands from central Brazil to the banks of the Parana River in northern Argentina.

An extraordinary creature of the Neotropical forests is that piglike animal, the peccary. True wild pigs never reached the southern continent (though settlers eventually brought the domesticated varieties), but the peccaries more than make up for the lack. There are two species, classified in a distinct family, the Tayassuidae, and although they are newcomers to the continent, the New World is the only place where they have survived into modern times—Europe and Asia know peccaries only as fossils.

Peccaries have a marked resemblance to the European wild boar, and one of the two species, the white-lipped peccary, is every bit as fierce and formidable an animal. White-lipped peccaries are big, standing nearly two feet high at the shoulder, and they are easily distinguished by the streak of white across their cheeks which gives them their name. They travel through the forest in bands ranging anywhere from 50 to 100 or more individuals, and fearless and aggressive as they are, they qualify as one of the more dangerous American mammals.

The second species, the collared peccary, is somewhat smaller, less aggressive and travels in bands of three to 25. Collared peccaries are quite commonly seen, rooting about for grubs and tubers, and range as far north as Arizona, New Mexico and Texas. This species can also be kept as a pet and, like a pig, is intelligent and affectionate when tamed.

What of that large and legendary order of mammals, the bats? In South America they have a particularly sinister reputation, including as they do the notorious vampires, which are reputed to suck their victims' blood. But where

HOW MANY POUNDS ON THE HOOF?

The bulkiest and the tiniest of the South American hoofed mammals (with a horse in the background for comparison) are the 400-pound Brazilian tapir, which stands 39 inches at the shoulder, and the 15-pound pudu, a deer barely 12 inches tall. The tapir inhabits lowland forests, its wedge-shaped head and heavy-set body being well adapted for plowing through the dense undergrowth. The tiny pudus range widely in the Andes, from high altitudes in Colombia to sea level in the forests of southern Chile.

do they belong in the geological history of the continent; when did they arrive?

This is a question which has no simple answer. Bats, like birds, can obviously get around by flying, but also like birds, they have fragile skeletons which do not fossilize well. The main center of bat evolution is thought to have been in the Old World tropics, and there is a greater range of divergent types there than in the New World. On the other hand, if one could make a list of the number of species of bats found on each of the continents (which would be difficult in our present state of knowledge), South America would very likely win —on the island of Trinidad, for example, 58 species have been classified.

Among the mammals, bats have a rather special geographic distribution, since they are not limited in their ranges by many of the physical barriers— large bodies of water, mountain ranges and others—that circumscribe the movements of nonflying creatures. This in turn opens up to them the possibility of radiating into a great variety of niches. And so indeed they have: in South America bats come in an impressive array of forms, from nectar-sippers which live like hummingbirds to fisheaters which skim the water like skipping stones to pluck fish out with their claws.

THE largest of the American bat families, which even includes a carnivorous species, is the Phyllostomatidae, or leaf-nosed bats. These get their name from an erect, bladelike structure that rises above the nostrils in almost all of the species, giving them an even more devilish appearance than that of other bats. The function of this "leaf" is not well understood, but it seems to have something to do with the echo location, or "sonar," system whereby bats find their way in the dark. One of the discoverers of this system, Donald R. Griffin of Harvard, went to Panama to study the behavior of this tropical group. Much to his surprise he was unable to pick up the cries of these bats with his usual instruments, though it was clear that they were navigating somehow by means of sound which bounced off objects in their path. When he tested leaf-nosed bats under the better-controlled conditions of his Harvard laboratory, he found that they were emitting softer cries, of a higher frequency, than those of northern bats. The bats seemed to get along just as well when the "leaf" was amputated; but watching the way in which the bats moved the nose-leaf as well as their ears in scanning sounds in the environment gave the definite impression that the nose-leaf was important somehow in the echo-location process.

The blood-lapping vampire bats of the American tropics are classified in a family by themselves (the Desmodontidae, with three genera) but they are thought to have evolved from their leaf-nosed relatives. These bats are major pests in many regions, killing smaller animals and weakening livestock by their bloodsucking habits. Even humans are not safe, although the bats are far from being as voracious as legend would have it—they do not puncture the skin of the throat but rather scrape any exposed patch of skin with their chisel-like teeth until the blood oozes out. They do this so gently that a sleeping animal or man is not awakened. The wound left by a vampire bat often continues to bleed for long afterward, and the discovery that rabies can be transmitted by the vampires has lent new importance to the study of these creatures.

Vampires are not the only bats which feed on blood. Some of the larger leaf-nosed bats will also lick blood from a wound, though they do not themselves bite their prey with a view to raising blood; they are largely insectivorous. The fact that vampires have adopted bloodsucking habits is actually further testimony to the extreme ranges of adaptation to which the bats have gone.

MARKED LIKE AN OCELOT BUT ABOUT THE SIZE OF A LARGE HOUSE CAT, THE MARGAY HUNTS SMALL ANIMALS IN THE NEOTROPICAL FOREST

Invaders from the North

When the American hemispheres were united by land two or three million years ago, an intermingling of animals followed. Some species moved north, but more evident was the movement south—for example, that of the carnivores and certain members of the camel family. The carnivores are still there in many forms, like the margay (above); the "camels" live on as the guanaco and vicuña.

A New Order of Predators

As part of the great southward movement of North American mammals, the large carnivores—bears, otters, dogs and cats—came across the land bridge to encounter the predaceous marsupials which had evolved on the isolated continent. The two orders met head on, and the carnivores prevailed after an evolutionary struggle much like that which is taking place in Australia today between native and imported species. The more efficient placental carnivores eventually replaced all but two of the South American marsupial families and ranged the forests, mountains and pampas of the continent. Now they, in turn, are being replaced by man, who is changing the countryside and exterminating whatever animals prey on his domestic stock. Large predators need large tracts to hunt in: the same square mile of land that supports thousands of lesser beasts may not be sufficient for more than one small cat, and so carnivorous animals like the big spotted cats playing below, the otter-shaped jaguarundi and the maned wolf are each becoming increasingly rare.

THE JAGUARUNDI is also known as the otter cat, not for any particular affinity it has for swimming—it lives in dry, thick underbrush—but for its long, low profile and for its otter size.

A MOTHER JAGUAR, BIGGEST OF THE NEW WORLD CATS, PLAYS WITH HER TWO CUBS. THE FATHER, LIKE AN ALLEY CAT, GENERALLY TAKES NO PAR

A MANED WOLF, named for the dark scruff of fur around its neck, stands panting on the savanna where it was run to exhaustion by men on horseback. An exceptionally shy, foxlike canine, it prowls by night and is rarely seen by man. Though known occasionally to attack stock, its usual diet is small animals—rats, frogs, snakes, birds—and even certain wild fruits.

RAISING THE LITTER. JAGUARS ARE BECOMING INCREASINGLY SCARCE BECAUSE THEY PREY ON CATTLE AND AS A RESULT ARE RUTHLESSLY HUNTED

THE VARIED BATS
OF TROPICAL AMERICA

Bats arrived in South America during the Tertiary and radiated widely, ultimately producing six families that are found nowhere else. Of these, the family Phyllostomidae is now the largest and most varied. Gathered in this drawing are representatives of each family: seven from the numerous Phyllostomidae (numbers 1, 2, 3, 6, 10, 11, 12), and one each from the other five. The wrinkle-faced bat (1) has a neck muff

which it folds up over its face when roosting. The long-tongued bat (2) hovers while feeding on nectar. The Honduran white bat (3) is one of several white species. The funnel-eared bat (4), like most bats, eats insects, while the Mexican bulldog bat (5) is remarkable for its ability to fish on the wing. The false vampire (6), America's biggest bat, shown killing a rat, attacks other bats as well, whereas the true vampire (7) stealth-ily drinks the blood from larger sleeping animals. The disk-winged bat (8) roosts upright, hanging by suction cups. The smoky bat (9), a rare Brazilian species, is the only member of its family. The fruit-eating bat (10) roosts on the underside of leaves, while the naked-backed bat (11) roosts in caves. The elaborate nose of the spear-nosed bat (12) is only one of many bizarre variants, as shown by other bats in this picture.

91

TWENTY MINUTES OLD AND STILL WET FROM ITS MOTHER'S TONGUE, A BABY VICUÑA IS CRADLED ON A PATCH OF SPRING SNOW IN THE ANDES

America's Camel Cousins

Strangely, no goat ever reached South America over the land bridge of Panama, nor any sheep or ox. Horses came but died out, for some unknown reason, before man arrived on the continent. Among the early immigrant mammals, there was only one group—the same that produced the Asian and African camels—whose descendants would eventually be valued by man for more than their carcasses. Just what these animals looked like we do not know, since their remains have never been found; they might even have appeared essentially the same as their descendants. One of these, the small, shy vicuña, dwells in the mountains, while the other, the guanaco, once roamed the pampas in great numbers. These two are still wild. Domestic forms, the llama and the alpaca, as shown in the genealogy chart at the right, were both bred from the guanaco by the pre-Incas. Between them, these two important ungulates, which supplied food, transportation and clothing, became staples of Andean civilization.

COMMON ANCESTOR

THE GUANACO, a wild animal, lives in small herds on the pampas. From it are descended both the llama and the alpaca. Its numbers have dwindled as man took over its range.

THE VICUÑA, also wild, is smaller than the guanaco and lives in the Andes just below the snow line. It is prized for its soft body hair, which makes the finest wool in the world.

THE LLAMA, a domestic version of the guanaco, was developed as a beast of burden by the pre-Incas, who bred it for size and strength. Llamas reach four and a half feet at the shoulder.

THE ALPACA, another domestic form of the guanaco, was bred for its long, soft hair, usually all white, brown or black. In the Andes it fills the role that wool sheep do in other lands.

SUPPLIER OF WOOL, this alpaca is sheared with a knife by two Peruvian women, much in the manner that Indians have always used. Though mules make better pack animals than llamas, and sheep, for their size, give more wool than alpacas, the native breeds are adapted to the thin Andean air and so are preferred by villagers like these, who live above 10,000 feet.

The Livestock of the Andes

For thousands of years before the Spaniards arrived with horses and mules, the llama was used to tote loads in a land where the wheel was still unknown. Moreover, it provided its masters with meat, while its hide was used for leather, its fat for candles, its droppings for fuel, and its hair for rope and cloth. Its shortcomings were only three: it was too weak to be ridden by a man, its milk sufficed only for its own young, and its wool, compared with that of the wild vicuña, was coarse. By breeding the smaller, finer-fleeced alpaca from the same strain, the Indians obtained better wool—but they were still walking and drinking water when the Spaniards arrived.

BEASTS OF BURDEN, a caravan of llamas stops to graze in front of an Inca ruin. Only males are worked. Beginning at age three, they will carry 50 to 100 pounds up to 15 miles a day.

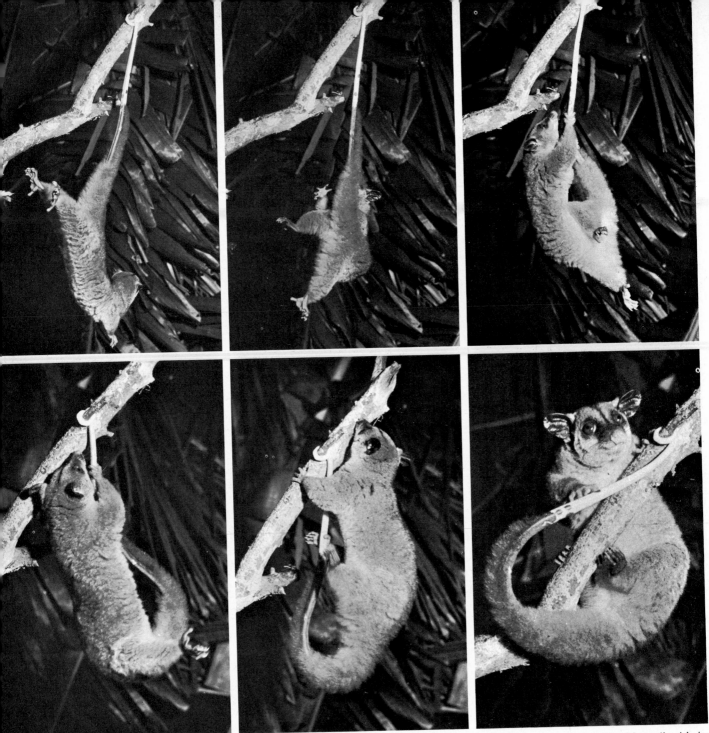

A WOOLLY OPOSSUM pulls itself up by its own bootstrap, as it were. Starting at top left, the animal is shown dangling by its tail alone. Seeking to get back up on the branch, it first jackknifes its body so that it can get hold of its tail with its forepaws (second and third pictures). Then it begins a hand-over-hand climb to regain the branch (bottom three pictures).

The South American Rope Trick

Among the different mammals, whether oldtimers or newcomers, there are more species with prehensile tails to be found in the Neotropical region than anywhere else in the world. Many of the primates have them; nearly all the marsupials and some edentates do. Even one carnivore, the kinkajou, seen hanging at the right, has a prehensile tail. An explanation is that in frequently flooded Amazonia, animals are faced with the alternatives sink, swim or climb. For those that chose to climb, scientists speculate, the tail thus took on a greater importance than it had in other, drier, less well-forested lands.

THE KINKAJOU, RELATED TO THE RACCOON, USES ITS TAIL AS A GRAPPLE WHEN MOVING AROUND IN

THE GIANT HARPY, most powerful of the world's eagles, terrorizes mammals and birds of the forest canopy. When it hunts, monkeys sometimes plummet like fruit from 120-foot trees, trying to escape it.

5

Where the Birds Are

SOUTH AMERICA has the most distinctive bird fauna of any of the continents—a wealth of different kinds unsurpassed anywhere. From the tip of Tierra del Fuego to central Mexico, almost two fifths of all known species of birds are represented: of the 27 orders of birds, 89 of the 155 families, an estimated 3,500 of the 8,600 species of birds on this planet which have been described. To give one striking example: the republic of Colombia alone, with 1,650 species of birds, about 1,500 of them breeders, has more than twice the number of bird species as the whole of North America north of Mexico.

No wonder this place is called "the bird continent!" From Patagonia to Yucatan it is bright with feathered creatures, from some of the biggest in the world to hummingbirds not much larger than bees.

Even the bird families that are not exclusive to South America have some highly interesting, in most cases endemic, genera and species there. Four of the six known species of flamingos, for instance, occur in South America. The duck tribe has such spectacular representatives as the black-necked swan, and such behaviorally interesting ones as the torrent duck, which earns its name by living in the roughest sort of mountain streams, and the steamer ducks, which

paddle like side-wheelers with their short wings. The heaviest of all eagles, the harpy, is South American, and so is the biggest of all storks, the jabiru. There are numerous songbirds—finches, grosbeaks, buntings, tanagers, warblers, orioles, wrens and thrushes. But the Neotropical region is unique in having an even greater number of birds classified as nonsingers. This gives the continent the undeserved reputation of being a place where birds, by and large, do not sing—the fact of the matter is that the scientific distinction between songbirds and nonsongbirds is a structural one having to do with the syrinx, and many of the so-called nonsingers have very sweet voices.

One reason for this extraordinary diversity of birds, of course, is the wide variety of habitats which South America offers, all the way from tropical rain forest, with its many opportunities for living and year-round favorable climate, to the broad grasslands of the savannas and pampas, the rocky mountain heights and the cool Patagonian and antarctic areas. Here, where a profusion of plants grows, lives a vast complex of animals, feeding off the plants and on each other, and here the birds find niches which are often narrow and sometimes call for specializations of a very high degree.

How they evolved these specializations and adapted to the various opportunities proffered for exploitation is largely unknown. Bird skeletons are light and fragile; as a consequence relatively few fossils of birds have been discovered in the South American region, so that the evolutionary history of the different orders and families cannot be worked out in anything like the detail possible with the mammals. However, it is safe to say that birds had acquired their modern characteristics by the time of the Eocene, 58 million years ago. In fact, Eocene fossils found elsewhere have been attributed to many families that still have living representatives—the penguins and ibises, for example.

IT seems probable, therefore, that South America had a diversified bird fauna even earlier, when the continent became separated from the other great land masses of the world at the turn of the Paleocene. These ancient birds were probably ancestors of many of the peculiar groups found today, flourishing and evolving in the long period of isolation. Whether, when that isolation was ended in the Pliocene, there was a wave of extinction comparable to that suffered by the mammals, we do not know. Doubtless the re-establishment of the land bridge brought its share of feathered as well as four-footed invaders from the north, but the numerous distinctive families and genera that still survive would seem to indicate that the birds held their own better than the mammals. In fact, they did even more—they sent many invaders of their own into the Northern Hemisphere, so that while siskins and perhaps a few other northern birds were working their way southward, tyrant flycatchers, tanagers and hummingbirds went north to become, like the ubiquitous opossum, familiar inhabitants of lands as far north as Canada. Today some of our most migratory land birds in North America belong to families that also occur, often in more varied forms, in South America—and this has led to the suggestion that such migrants may have been originally South American species which took to seasonally flying northward when the recession of the ice ages changed the climate there.

Certainly one reason why more northern birds did not take hold as permanent residents in South America is the enormous extent of the tropical rain forest. Here was a combination of climate and vegetation that had no counterpart in temperate North America at all, and it lay like a barrier across almost the entire northern part of the continent. To birds from North America, mainly species of

HOW THE POTOO GROWS

The melancholy cries of the common potoo, a relative of the whippoorwill, can be heard between dawn and dusk in the forests of Central and South America. In the daytime, however, this mottled grayish-brown bird escapes detection by drawing its body up straight and thin, and sitting motionless with its eyes almost closed, so that it resembles the stub of a branch. It lays a single egg in a hollow and, within one or two days after hatching, the fluffy nestling begins to take the peculiar adult pose. Growing up on the spot where the egg was laid, it, too, is a perfectly camouflaged "stub."

open country or coniferous or deciduous woodland, the rain forest was a most inhospitable breeding place; it also was crowded with better-adapted competitors, for to native species it had offered a chance for unparalleled development. For all their powers of flight, most birds are stay-at-homes, and even highly migratory species tend to come back to the same nesting area year after year. Many sedentary forms restrict themselves to one side of a large river, or one valley in a particular mountain range or one isolated mountain peak. In the year-round favorable conditions of the humid tropical forest, with its great variety of vegetation, species have been able to evolve within narrow niches, and allied forms have been able to survive with considerable overlap in habitat.

A GOOD example of the extraordinary avian diversification in South America is that of the hummingbirds. There are 319 species of hummingbirds, all of them found only in the New World and most of them found only in South America. Many have narrowly restricted ranges. A mere 18 species have been recorded as far north as the United States, and only one, the rubythroat, reaches the eastern states. One species, the rufous hummingbird, breeds as far north as Alaska, which is about as far away from the tropical rain forest as it is possible to get. Hummingbirds must have been around for a very long time to allow for the evolution of so many species.

Other widely diversified South American groups are the ovenbirds (215 species), tanagers (222 species), tyrant flycatchers (365 species) and antbirds (222 species). Many of the families are extremely interesting—the hoatzin, for instance, was thought by William Beebe to be "probably the most remarkable and interesting bird living on earth today," and it is a good example of the peculiarities of avian life that may be found in and around the rain forest.

Taxonomically, the hoatzin, a pheasant-sized bird that lives along the banks of tropical streams, is in a family and suborder all by itself. It is hard to classify as a bird; it has a musky body odor and, with the ability of its young to crawl with clawed wings and feet as well as swim, it is reminiscent of the first bird, *Archaeopteryx*, a reptilian creature. Its flight is heavy and clumsy, and invariably ends in a crash landing which dishevels its already loose and disordered feathers completely. The hoatzin is really a better climber than flier, but in which direction it is evolving, no one can say. Hoatzin survival appears to depend to a great extent on community living in which "families" of birds ranging from two to six members share nest building and incubation duties and also care of the young.

The visitor to the rain forest is at first not particularly conscious of birds, or indeed of animals of any kind. They are there in endless variety, but they have to be looked for. The forest is dark and quiet: the many-layered canopy of trees of different sizes filters out the sunlight, leaving the wooded depths bathed in a cathedral-like gloom. The cathedral effect is heightened by the columnar trunks of the trees, often with great buttresses formed by the roots, architectural detail being added by the woody vines—the lianas—that are pressed sculpture-like against the trunks, contributing perhaps a third of the foliage above. So little light reaches the ground that few plants can actually grow there. As a result the forest is open, with little undergrowth.

Here in this extraordinary world of hush and gloom, the birds live in environmental layers as pronounced as those on the sides of a mountain. Each layer provides a complexity of niches for the animal inhabitants. In a study of the ecology of birds in a tropical wet forest area in Costa Rica, the ornithologist Paul

A STREAMSIDE BABY

Hoatzins live along tropical streams where arum plants provide them with their favorite diet. They have extremely large crops for storage and partial digestion of the arum leaves. In the nesting season, the piping cries of the young induce the adult to regurgitate some of this mushy substance, which the baby then takes from its mouth (top). The position of the nest over the stream provides a clear escape path for the young hoatzin. When threatened, it drops in the water (bottom), swims downstream and takes refuge in the tangled growth along the bank.

Slud found that he could distinguish five different layers, or zones, each with a distinctive set of bird inhabitants. These were (1) the forest floor; (2) the understory, reaching up to about 15 feet above the ground; (3) the middle forest canopy, extending from 15 feet to heights of 50 to 75 feet; (4) the main forest canopy, formed by the treetops; (5) the free air above the forest.

Few such studies of the many-layered bird life in the tropics have been made, and although Slud's observations reflect a local situation, they illustrate the general principle of stratification. Here in this Costa Rican forest, he found that 14 bird species lived mainly on the forest floor and that six more species regularly dropped down to the ground to forage. The lower understory actually had two sets of characteristic inhabitants: some 18 species foraging at about eye-level height of a human observer, and 59 species which occurred in the larger shrubs and small trees growing up to about the 15-foot level. The middle forest canopy had 68 species, the upper canopy 69, and in the open air above the forest regularly flew 20 species of hawks, vultures, parrots and swifts.

The most characteristically Neotropical inhabitants of the forest floor and undergrowth are the antbirds. These occur nowhere else in the world. Their 222 species are mostly starling-size or smaller, and most of them live in deep forest, where they often blend so well with their background that they are difficult to see. They get their name because some of the species make their living, in a manner of speaking, from the swarms of army ants that forage through the forest. Though legend has magnified the ferocity and destructive power of the army ants far beyond what they really are capable of, they are formidable enough to their invertebrate prey. As they advance in broad and sinuous columns, they explore every nook and cranny of the forest floor so thoroughly that they flush all kinds of insects and other creatures out of their hiding places—and it is these that are the principal food of the antbirds, not the ants themselves.

Antbirds are not the only birds that take advantage of the forays of the army ants, but they are perhaps the only ones who exploit *only* this particular source of food. Usually they stay with the same swarms of ants throughout the two weeks or so of their foraging expeditions. In his Costa Rican forest, Slud found three species of antbirds always associated with the ants; he also found as regular participants a ground cuckoo (*Neomorphus*), several woodcreepers and certain types of tanagers. Like the antbirds themselves, these birds habitually perched a little way above and ahead of the advancing ant swarm, but unlike the antbirds, they did not regularly remain with the swarm throughout the two weeks or so of periodic ant activity. Once the ants passed out of their territory, they returned to their normal ways of feeding, whereas the antbirds would hunt a new column of ants and associate themselves with it.

SHARING the forest floor with the antbirds are various species of tinamous, another characteristically South American group of birds, which range widely from Patagonia to Mexico. Tinamous surely belong among the real old-timers on the South American continent. There are 45 known species of them, and they are so different from other birds in anatomical structure that they have had to be classified in a separate order—their nearest relatives are probably the ostrichlike rheas of the Argentine plains. To North Americans, they would probably look something like quail or guinea fowl. They have many quail-like habits—notably that of remaining perfectly quiet in the presence of danger, relying on camouflage for protection. In the forest species, the plumage blends completely with the leafy floor; in the grassland types, it usually is adapted to the colorations of the range. One tinamou was once observed crouched in a field of newly sprouting winter wheat: completely unaware that it stood out like a brown blob against the bright green background, it stayed immobile and was caught by hand.

The tinamous are among the birds that leave the care of the young to the male. Before the eggs are laid, the male shapes what seems to be a sort of nest—a scratched-out hollow often so rudimentary that some ornithologists would not classify it as a nest at all. The eggs themselves are strikingly beautiful, with polished shells that gleam like porcelain. The male does all the incubating and later on herds the young about until they are able to fly. The females are usually larger than the males, and have a reputation for carefree and promiscuous sexual behavior which they do not entirely deserve. In certain species, each male has several females which lay eggs in one nest for him, and only when he is busy incubating the eggs do they look for other males to repeat the process.

THE manakins, another family of undergrowth dwellers which are exclusive to the South American region, show the opposite kind of behavior and often are also at the other extreme of appearance from the drab tinamous. Some of them are among the gaudiest little birds known. Small, usually exceedingly colorful, males often congregating in groups, they are lively and entertaining to watch. The males leave all of the chores of nest building and child rearing to the females. Males of many species are known to have complicated and very acrobatic group mating dances, often accompanied by loud cracks or snaps, in some cases performed up in the trees or shrubbery, in other cases in special display areas on the ground. The areas of the golden-collared manakin are carefully cleared of all debris, and when a female turns up, a whole group of males, each on his own little dance floor, puts on a frantic show with firecrackerlike snappings of the wings until the female has chosen her partner.

The greatest variety of birds is found in the upper forest canopy and on the forest border, where flowers bloom and fruit abounds. Here they come literally in all colors, kinds and sizes. There are hummingbirds, parrots, cotingas, tanagers, honeycreepers and toucans. They are specialized for all manners of food getting, from catching insects to penetrating the complicated structures of flowers for the extraction of nectar. One group of honeycreepers, the flower piercers (*Diglossa*), shows a characteristically peculiar bill especially designed to pierce flowers: the upper mandible is upturned and hooked so that it can hold the corolla tube of a blossom while the lower mandible pierces it, allowing the slender tongue to reach in to extract the nectar.

No treatment of South American birds can overlook its most characteristic family of songbirds, the tanagers. These are widely distributed, but are most numerous in the canopy of the rain forest and along the forest edge, and are probably the most brilliantly colored of all songbird families. There are more than 200 species, four of which reach the United States, and they show great variations in pattern, color and bill shape. Some are clothed in exquisite opalescent hues, some combine a variety of bright, rich colors. They are usually rather poor singers, but a few have loud and striking chants. The genus *Tangara* (formerly known as *Calliste*, or "most beautiful"), includes a truly fantastic variety of colorful birds, among which the females wear essentially the same garb as the males. This latter is not as unusual in tropical birds as in the brightly colored birds of temperate climates; in fact, males and females of many nonsinging birds in South America often share their duties as well as their colors.

A COMMUNAL WEAVER

Oropendolas are noted for their elaborate pouch nests and sometimes drape a single tree with scores of them, each about three feet long. The nest of the crested species shown here is woven of leaf fibers and vine stems by the female. She is courted by males which sing and perform headlong dances, sometimes on the structure itself. Males guard the community, but will have nothing to do with nest building or family raising.

THE SHAPING OF A TAIL

The blue-crowned motmot, a jay-sized bird common throughout the tropical forests, has a remarkable tail. Near the tips of the two long, central tail feathers, the barbs are more weakly attached to the shaft and eventually drop off under continued preening by the bird's bill. The result is a tail that looks like a pair of miniature tennis rackets and is frequently swung back and forth like a pendulum.

The most spectacular of the high-canopy birds, however, are probably the toucans. The outstanding feature of a toucan is its enormous bill, which often looks like a bill flying through the woods with a bird attached. In some species it is literally almost as big as the bird itself. Huge and often brightly colored as it is, its uses could be many and varied, and there is no agreement on why it evolved as it did. Some think it is an ornament or means of species recognition, some an instrument of intimidation—toucans have, for instance, been observed robbing hawks' nests after chasing the parents away. But although it is very light in weight, the bill is also fairly strong, and it seems most likely that it serves a function in pulling off from the branches of the trees the fruits and berries that constitute much of toucan food.

There are 37 known species of toucans, all of them tropical American and many of them inhabitants of the Amazon forest. They are for the most part gregarious birds, living in flocks much after the fashion of crows—and, like crows, they sometimes gang up on any bird of prey that comes near. They nest in holes in trees. When sleeping, a toucan folds its tail over its back and tucks its bill under a wing. Like parrots, toucans are easily domesticated and make affectionate and lively pets.

Parrots are not exclusively Neotropical—they reach their greatest variety in Australia and New Guinea—but there are enough of them in the tropical American forests as well as in more open country to make them an outstanding part of the local avifauna. In forests they spend most of their time in the upper levels of the canopy and are most often seen flying above the tops of the trees, moving in noisy flocks from one feeding area to another. The most spectacular are the macaws, aflame with color, from the brilliant red of the scarlet macaw to the blue of the hyacinth species. There are also many smaller parakeets, including the monk parakeet of Argentina, the only parrot that lives communally in large apartment-house nests built of twigs in treetops or on tops of telegraph poles.

THE largest and fiercest inhabitant of the upper canopy is certainly the harpy eagle, a most unusual bird of prey which feeds on monkeys, sloths, agoutis and an occasional opossum or porcupine. Weighing some 20 pounds and with short, powerful wings, the harpy displays extraordinary maneuverability in pursuing its victims through the trees. One observer watching a harpy chasing a capuchin monkey estimated that it flew at 40 to 50 miles per hour, dodging tree trunks and branches; on another occasion, a harpy was seen to roll over completely onto its back to pluck a monkey from underneath the branch on which it had sought refuge. Big as they are, these eagles are almost never seen flying above the canopy of the rain forest and rarely have they been found to hunt in the open savanna.

High above the parrots and hawks, over the topmost canopy of the trees, cruise the soaring vultures. The New World varieties of these big carrion eaters are sufficiently different from their Old World relatives to be classified as a separate family, and by some as a distinct suborder. There are six American species, of which five occur in the Neotropical region. The only one now restricted to North America is the California condor, which is almost extinct. The widest-ranging member of the family is the turkey vulture, a sizable bird with a wingspread of up to six feet and an easily recognizable naked red head and neck. Turkey vultures are characteristic of the tropical forests, but they also breed as far north as New England and Canada, where they stay all summer, many flying southward beyond Panama in the fall to wintering grounds still unknown.

The biggest of all the vultures, the Andean condor, is also one of the biggest of all flying birds: its wing span of as much as 10 feet is exceeded only by that of the largest albatrosses, which have the typically longer and narrower wing of ocean soarers. Like all vultures, the condor is a carrion feeder, although the Andean species may sometimes take live prey in the form of helpless or new-born animals. The condor in his soaring flight is one of the most highly specialized birds aloft.

Becoming airborne is the condor's only stage of awkwardness; a heavy bird (up to 25 pounds) with typically weak feet, it has to run to get up flying speed in the thin air of its high-altitude habitat. On flat ground, it may require 40 to 50 feet, and even then may touch down once or twice before it is really flying. Then, with slow, powerful wing flaps, it gains altitude until it reaches the point where it can soar on rising currents, circling higher and higher on wings that are almost motionless. Indeed, in comparison to the smaller turkey vultures and hawks, the condor looks like a fixed-wing airplane and has sometimes been mistaken for one. Though it usually forages at elevations of around 500 feet above ground, it has been encountered at 3,000 feet or even higher—which, in its mountain habitat, might mean up to 16,000 feet above sea level.

On the slopes of the mountains the character of the forest changes with altitude, and the animal life in it changes too. Gradually, as the air grows cooler with height, the forest shows subtropical and temperate species. Somewhere in the neighborhood of 2,000 to 3,000 feet a new influence enters, particularly in mountains that are close to the sea. This is fog, forming when the moisture in the air cools and condenses as it rises up the flanks of the mountains toward the peaks. Here is the region of the so-called "cloud forest," an environment as distinctive as the rain forest—and the long backbone of the Andes from Mexico to Tierra del Fuego gives the Neotropical region a larger area of cloud forest than any other place in the world.

Cloud forest is, in general, less high and dense than lowland rain forest, and as a result of the perpetual moisture, rocks and soil and even trees are covered with a rich growth of mosses. Epiphytes like orchids grow in profusion—not just the shy, peeping types of other tropical areas but some of the gaudiest known. In fact, the visitor to the cloud forest may get the impression that almost everything that lives here tends to have brighter colors than elsewhere. Here live some of the most startlingly brilliant of the tropical butterflies and here, too, is the habitat of most species of those extraordinary little winged creatures, the hummingbirds.

Nothing on earth quite compares, in color, acrobatics and miniature perfection of adaptation, with the hummingbirds. Audubon called them "glittering fragments of the rainbow," and indeed this is what they appear to be as they flash through the forest, the light refracting in constantly changing iridescent colors from their wings and bodies. These tiny creatures—"flower kissers," as they are known in Brazil—are an entirely American phenomenon, and by far the majority of species are tropical. Of these most are forest dwellers, where flowers and their nectar are available in plenty.

Many things about hummingbirds are remarkable, if not unique. They are, for instance, the only birds that have been proved to be able to fly backwards and sideways and hover motionless like miniature helicopters for indefinite periods. This, as the hummingbird expert and photographer Crawford H. Greenewalt discovered, is due to the fact that their wings do double duty:

THE BELLBIRDS

Among the most bizarrely ornamented members of the cotinga family are the bellbirds, named for their explosive metallic peals that can resound half a mile through the forest. The male bearded bellbird (above) has a large cluster of stringy wattles hanging from its throat. The male three-wattled bellbird has only three, but these swell up and lengthen dramatically when it calls. Both voice and wattles probably attract the females.

whereas most birds derive power only on the downstroke of the wing, hummingbirds derive it on the upstroke as well. This, in turn, has resulted in abnormally powerful flight muscles and wing structure in relation to the rest of their bodies. Hummingbirds are an exception to an almost universal rule among animals which says that the body weight is proportional to the cube of a linear dimension—i.e., an increase in body size results in a threefold increase in the length of, say, an arm or a limb. In hummingbirds, the increase would be sixfold, so that a hummingbird the size of a swan, for example, would have a wing span of 65 feet. As it is, their size range is so relatively small—from about eight and a half inches for the biggest to two and a fourth inches for the smallest—that the proportionate differences in wing size are scarcely noticeable.

The brilliant iridescence shown by most hummingbird species has long intrigued scientists. Many explanations have been offered, and curiously enough, one of the first—proposed two and a half centuries ago—was the right one, although scientific limitations made its proof impossible until about 50 years ago. In his *Treatise on Opticks*, Sir Isaac Newton wrote: "The finely coloured feathers of some birds . . . do in the very same part of the Feather appear of several Colours in several position of the Eye, after the very same manner that thin Plates were found to do . . . and therefore arise from the thinness of the transparent parts of the Feathers; that is, from the slenderness of the very fine Hairs, or *Capillamenta*, which grow out of the sides of the grosser lateral branches or fibres of those Feathers." In other words—as can now be proven by the electron microscope—the colors of the hummingbird are so-called "interference colors," caused by the same optical phenomenon as that seen on the surface of a soap bubble or in oil floating in water. The colored portions of the feathers, most often those of head, neck and chest but also frequently of flight feathers in wings and tail, are covered with a film of tiny elliptical platelets so infinitely small that only the electron microscope can show them. It is this reflective film which produces the astonishingly pure spectral colors seen in the changing light as a hummingbird flicks past.

T HERE are other brilliant birds in the cloud forest, notably some Neotropical members of the trogon family, which are more numerous here than in either tropical Africa or Asia. All the species are spectacularly colored, the males varying from metallic or golden green to violet on the upper parts of their bodies and from bright reds through oranges to yellows below. In all, there are some 20 species of trogon from Arizona southward through the continent—and of them all, the best known is the quetzal, the sacred bird of the Aztecs.

The quetzal inhabits cloud forests from Mexico to Panama. Its coloring is flamboyant: golden-green head, neck, back and wings, a red belly and white tail feathers. But its most conspicuous attribute is its long train of curved, green feathers, which sets it apart from all other trogon species. Its plumes were used in Aztec ceremonies. Today it is the national bird of Guatemala, chosen not only for its beauty but as a symbol of freedom, for according to legend the bird could not live in captivity. The Aztecs and Mayas worshiped the quetzal as the god of air. It can and does survive in modern zoos, but in the wild it is rarely seen. Its numbers have dwindled not so much because of hunting—although plumage pirates took their toll—but because of the steady destruction of its forest range. Quetzals require a continuous supply of small fruits for their food, and this means that large areas of forest are needed to support them. In the forest, the birds nest in dead trees or holes in dead limbs, and the male, despite its fine plumage, takes an active part in all housekeeping chores.

In northern South America and along the inner slopes of the Peruvian and Colombian Andes live two species of the cotinga family, cocks-of-the-rock that rival the quetzal in brightness of color. The male of the Guianan species is a bright orange-gold, the Andean type more reddish; the females in both cases are a plain dark brown. The sight of one of the males against the background of forest green is a memorable experience. One ordinarily prosaic naturalist was moved to call it "a mass of brilliant flame"; another, seeing a cock-of-the-rock in flight, likened it to "a fiery comet."

For a long time little was known about the cock-of-the-rock, for the cloud forest in which the birds live is remote and still difficult of access. In 1915 The American Museum of Natural History in New York finally sent an expedition to southern Colombia with the primary objective of obtaining specimens of the birds and learning something about their nesting habits, which were almost entirely unknown. The nests were located at last high on the cliffs of a river gorge, as inaccessible a location as could be imagined. Nearby the expedition members found the small, cleared areas in the forest where the males perform the mating dances which were observed by the naturalist Richard Schomburgk, traveling in British Guiana a century and a quarter ago.

SCHOMBURGK described the dance in a passage which has since become an ornithological classic, the accuracy of which is now fully confirmed. "While about a score of birds perched upon the bushes surrounding the playground," he wrote, "were uttering the most peculiar notes, and apparently constituting an admiring audience, one of the males was cutting capers on the smooth boulder; in proud consciousness of self it cocked and dropped its outspread tail and flapped its likewise expanded wings, and thus continued to figure out the steps until it seemed to be exhausted, when it flew back onto the bush and its place was taken by another male. The females in the meanwhile uttered a peculiar note, watched unweariedly and on the return of the tired performer uttered a scream denoting applause." Proof came in 1961, when the late E. Thomas Gilliard studied these brilliant arena birds in the field.

There are many other brightly colored inhabitants of both cloud forest and rain forest—the jacamars, for example, which with their shining, metallic-green backs and long bills look like oversized hummingbirds; or the motmots, most varied in Central America, with their long, often racket-shaped tails, which are formed when the barbs of the two middle feathers between the basal part and the tip of the tail drop off as the bird preens itself.

Somewhat less distinctive than the birds of the forest are those of South America's grasslands and open country. The outstanding bird, the very symbol of the pampas, is the rhea, that large, flightless type which is so reminiscent of Africa's ostrich or the Australian emu. In the details of their structure, however, all three are different and form separate orders. The rhea is the smallest of the three, but is still a formidable bird, weighing up to 50 pounds and standing four to five feet tall.

Rheas live in polygamous family groups, with one male dominating a harem of a half dozen or so females. Their nests are shallow depressions scratched in the soil, and since all the females of a harem lay in the same nest, one such family home may contain 50 or more eggs. And it is the male who has to incubate them once they are laid—another instance in which the females for some reason have managed to avoid what men like to consider natural female duties. The rhea of

THE UMBRELLABIRD

An even stranger cotinga is the bare-necked umbrellabird. The male of this species has a luxuriant crest of feathers that can be spread like a canopy over its eyes and most of the beak (above). Its throat is a mass of wrinkled scarlet skin from which hangs a single feather-tipped wattle. To produce its booming call, the bird inflates the loose skin into an air sac resembling a large ripe tomato (below), then deflates before calling again.

the pampas is the most common species of the order, but there is a smaller one, the lesser, or Darwin's, rhea, which lives in Patagonia and also has a distinct race in the mountains of Peru and Bolivia, sharing the habitat of the condor.

Birds of the South American grasslands often are reminiscent of North American birds, reflecting the similarity of habitat. The grasslands, too, are the wintering grounds of many migratory North American shorebirds and a few songbirds as well. Relatives of the northern sparrows, blackbirds, hawks, meadowlarks, swans, rails, ibises, ducks and grebes can be found here, along with a wide variety of Neotropical ovenbirds. These latter, which derive their name from the fact that some species build ovenlike nests of mud, have radiated into a wide range of niches which include every habitat from sea level to alpine plateaus. The more open country is also the home of such distinctive long-legged birds as the seriema and the screamer.

Many pampas birds are large in size, an advantage in the open country, where size not only facilitates the covering of large areas in search of food but also the recognizing of one's own kind and of one's enemies.

IN this discussion of South American birds, nothing has been said so far about water birds or sea birds. Of fresh-water birds there are many, associated with the endless marshes, swamps and river systems that cover so much of the continent, including the jabiru stork. But for the most part, they belong to the same groups that are found in other parts of the world and show much the same habits. One exception is the sunbittern, a slender heronlike bird that lives along streams in heavy forests or in wooded swamps. It is not closely related to the ordinary bitterns, or in fact to any other known bird. Anatomically it stands apart, its closest known relative perhaps being the curious kagu, another odd fellow found only on the Pacific island of New Caledonia. Both the sunbittern and the kagu are classified in families by themselves and are presumed to be the last relics of types that have otherwise become extinct.

As for sea birds, all known families except the northern loons and auks are represented. Penguins abound in the cold southern waters and islands and even reach the equator in the Galápagos Archipelago.

But while the South American sea birds may not be strikingly different from those of other southern and subantarctic regions, the continent does have a unique environment in the bird islands of Peru. Off these small islands near the coast, the cold upwelling waters of the Humboldt Current form one of the richest fishing grounds of any ocean, where sea birds have been congregating in untold millions for no one knows how many thousands of years, and in the rainless climate their excrement has accumulated to form great beds of guano—the finest plant fertilizer known.

The Incas knew about guano. They developed a highly sophisticated system of agriculture with terraced fields and carefully planned irrigation systems, and used the guano of the islands in producing their rich crops. But the agricultural system broke down with the Spanish conquest, which concentrated on gold rather than farming, and the use of guano was forgotten. In 1804 Alexander von Humboldt, who noticed everything, brought a sample of guano back to Europe and its fabulous properties as a fertilizer were rediscovered. In the century that followed, the guano and the birds were exploited so ruthlessly that the Peruvian government finally was forced to organize a guano administration and start enforcing protection for the islands, which still today are one of the most valuable national assets of Peru.

THE BLUE-GRAY TANAGER, LIKE MANY TROPICAL SONGBIRDS, HAS BRIGHT PLUMAGE BUT ITS THIN AND WAVERING VOICE IS DISAPPOINTING

A Bounty of Birds

Latin America's bird life is the richest and most distinctive in the world. More than 25 families are peculiar to this region alone, including toucans, cotingas and jacamars of fabulous colors, and such primitives as the hoatzin, the seriema and the flightless rhea. Others—hummingbirds, flycatchers and tanagers—had their origin in the equatorial belt but have since spread into North America.

THE COCK-OF-THE-ROCK is the most brilliant of a bright-colored family, the cotingas, which numbers 90 species. The males and females live separately, the drab-feathered females in sheltered areas where they build big nests of mud pellets. In display arenas on the forest floor several hundred feet away, the males dance and posture during the mating season.

Varied Birds
for Varied Niches

There are several reasons for the richness of bird life in the American tropics. First: there is a wide variety of habitats to suit a wide variety of birds. Second: the largest habitat—the rain forest—is the most complex and varied known on this planet, and it alone offers an incredible number of niches to birds.

A JACAMAR hawks an insect against a clay bank. There are 15 species of jacamars, most of them having the metallic look of large hummingbirds.

A SCYTHEBILL, one of 48 woodpeckerlike birds known as woodcreepers, does not use its bill as a chisel but as a deep probe for insects in air plants.

A SERIEMA ventures from dense underbrush to catch a lizard or a small snake. It belongs to a family of long-legged birds which are peculiar to tropical America and which seem to be dying out; only two species remain.

Third: much of the continent enjoys warm weather the year round; most birds do not have to migrate to escape severe winter conditions. Fourth: habitats tend to be broken up and isolated from each other, an important factor in the evolution of species. Lastly, climatic catastrophes like the ice ages had little effect in tropical America and thus caused no mass extinctions as in the Northern Hemisphere. The result: not only more kinds of birds than in other continents, but more kinds found nowhere else. Shown here is a sampling of only four of the 2,000-odd species that live only in tropical America.

THE SUNBITTERN, although it is a shy, solitary bird like the true bitterns, and shares their habit of spearing frogs and minnows, actually belongs to an entirely different and ancient family of tropical American birds—and is the last surviving member of its line. It lives on wooded stream banks from Mexico to southern Brazil, but its retiring ways make it hard

to see; thus it is often thought to be a good deal scarcer than it really is. It gets its name from the sunburst of tawny orange and gold made visible by the wing display shown here. When-ever it is excited, the sunbittern will spread its wings in this fashion, holding them outstretched for several minutes while it dances about agitatedly. Why it does this is not known.

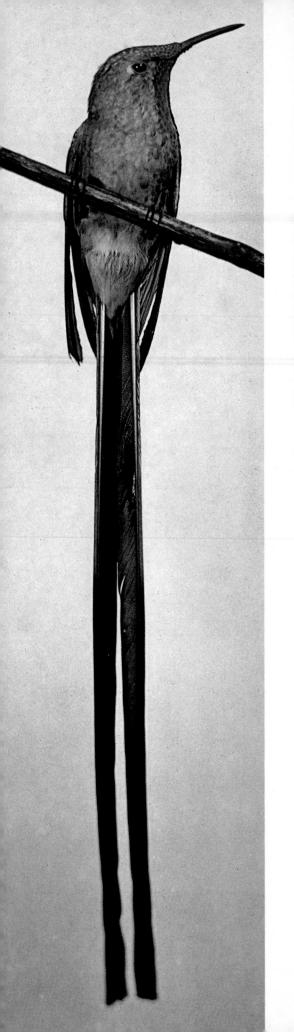

THE APTLY NAMED GIANT HUMMINGBIRD, SHOWN LIFE SIZE, IS THE WORLD'S LARGEST. IT AL

Jewels of the Tropics

Hummingbirds as a family occur in all climates of the Western Hemisphere wherever there are flowers to sip, but the vast majority of them are crowded into tropical Central and South America. More than 300 species have been identified there, and their living habits closely studied. Highly individualistic, hummingbirds have been found to be polygamous and promiscuous, often interbreeding with abandon, which has led to interesting hybrid species. But the females, once bred, become dedicated and skillful nest builders and, later, diligent mothers. Though expending prodigious amounts of energy themselves in the constant fury of their flight, they manage all alone to nourish their young with regurgitated food, boldly defending them against intruders.

STREAMER TAIL of the male black-tailed trainbearer is more than twice as long as its body. The usefulness of such long tails is questionable; they presumably are attractive to females.

SLOWEST WINGBEAT OF ANY HUMMINGBIRD, 25 A SECOND, COMPARED TO 80 FOR SMALLER ONES

ONE OF THE TINIEST HUMMERS, ALSO LIFE SIZE, IS THE BRAZILIAN AMETHYST

THE LONGEST BILL, three to four inches, belongs to the Andean swordbill. Hummers are aggressive birds; they dive at each other and even buzz hawks 100 times their size.

AWAKE AND STRETCHING, a hooded visor-bearer fans its tail, and the feathers shine with a ruby glow. When the tail is folded (*opposite*), it appears to be black. Named by the natu- ralist John Gould for its brilliant green face mask, this visor-bearer was thought extinct for 50 years, but in 1959 specimens were found living among the rocks of Minas Gerais, Brazil.

PUFFED-UP throat feathers of a sleeping visor-bearer reflect a different light from those of the bird opposite and look gray instead of green.

Hummingbirds: Tiny Dynamos

Intensely active during most of their waking hours, hummingbirds put out more energy for their size than any other warm-blooded animal. Compared to that of a hummingbird, a man's metabolism is slow and inefficient beyond belief. Running as fast as he can, a man consumes—for his size—only a tenth the energy that a hovering hummingbird would, and he tires much more quickly. To fuel their minute but efficient furnaces, some hummingbirds eat half their weight in sugar daily and must also have some protein in the form of insects. Measured in human terms, this food intake is the equivalent of 285 pounds of hamburger a day.

A hummingbird has about a thousand feathers, half as many as a robin-sized bird, and a tenth as many as a chicken. But it is so much smaller that it is actually the most densely plumaged of all birds. Its scintillating feathers are structured in such a way as to reflect and scatter the light, like oil on water, making the bird gleam with iridescence and often change color entirely as it moves (left and above).

SEXUAL DIFFERENCES are marked in most hummingbirds. The female topaz from Brazil (top) has greenish plumage, but the male has a red and gold body and long, forked tail feathers.

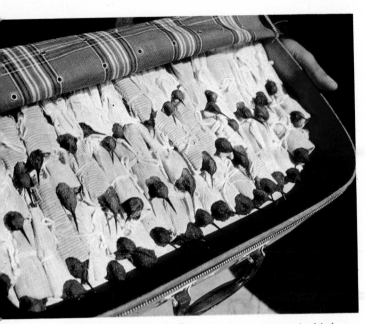

IN CLOTH STRAITJACKETS, some 40 live hummingbirds are packed in a suitcase for travel. They suffer no ill effects from this, and Ruschi has sent them by jet as far away as Portugal.

To Catch a Hummingbird

Much of our knowledge of hummingbirds comes from 30 years of observation by the Brazilian naturalist Augusto Ruschi, who has studied them in large open-air aviaries in the mountain village of Santa Teresa.

To catch a hummingbird, Ruschi places a decoy —a live pygmy owl, the natural enemy of hummingbirds—in a tree and waits below, holding a 30-foot aluminum rod smeared with sticky oil. When he whistles like an owl, an angry throng of hummingbirds gathers, attempting to mob the decoy. Ruschi slowly swishes his pole back and forth, and any hummingbird that touches it will become stuck in the oil like a large insect. Ruschi carefully removes it, cleans and dries it, and inserts its head through a slit in a piece of cloth, which is gently wrapped around the bird's body. It can then be handled easily and fed, from time to time, by inserting its bill in a flask of 20 per cent sugar solution.

Without an owl decoy, a hummingbird would be very hard to catch with a sticky pole; it is much too swift and agile. Under ordinary back-yard conditions, a hummer will hover and feed within a few inches of people, secure in its ability to escape. Its reaction time is a mere 20 milliseconds, and its breakaway (*right*) takes only a fifth of a second.

AGILITY IN FLIGHT is demonstrated by a dusky jacobin, a common Brazilian species. This bird has been hovering while feeding at a nectar tube, but has been startled by the sound

of the camera. The photograph catches it as it flicks its tail open into a fan and with arched body begins to zoom up and over onto its back. This is the quickest way for it to change direction, and it will then flip over onto its belly and dart away. The entire maneuver takes only a fraction of a second and is executed so rapidly that it cannot be followed by the eye.

BIGGEST AND SMALLEST EGGS in the Western Hemisphere are those of a rhea and a hummingbird. The difference in length, about 10 to 1, is almost the same as the relative heights of the adults. Palatable as well as big, the rhea egg makes an elegant soufflé. After the top is cut off, the contents, still in the shell, are mixed with sugar and baked in hot ashes.

A Vanishing Dweller of the Pampas

Five feet tall and weighing as much as 50 pounds, the flightless rhea is a lightweight compared to the seven-foot African ostrich, which weighs up to 300 pounds. But its size still makes it a conspicuous target on the pampas. Argentine Indians once pursued rheas on foot as a food source, but after 1850, European settlers sought their hides for rugs and their feathers for dusters. Roving gauchos learned to run down the birds on cow ponies and lasso them with *bolas*, leather thongs whose weighted ends entangled their long legs and neck. Finally, the conversion of the pampas into the wheat and cattle belt of South America has been even more devastating than hunting or trapping. Fencing, in particular, bothers them, tangling them in wires and preventing them from traveling.

A MALE RHEA OPENS ITS BILL TO UTTER A BOOMING CALL. FEMALES ARE SILENT

FLEEING RHEAS, camouflaged by their mist-gray plumes, melt into the distance. They run as swiftly as African ostriches (40 miles per hour) and, like the Australian emus, are strong swimmers. When pressed, rheas also have the curious habit of doubling back on their tracks and falling flat in the tall grasses, a tactic which makes them extremely difficult to find.

A Glimpse into the Past

Some birds still show traces of their reptilian ancestry by hatching with rudimentary claws on their wings. These usually drop off in infancy. In only a few species do the young actually use them as aids in clambering about in thickets. One such is the hoatzin, an extremely primitive fowl-like bird of the Amazon and Orinoco riverbanks. A few hours after birth, a hoatzin chick can leave its nest and take up an acrobatic existence in the thick tangle of arum bushes that lines tropical rivers. The hoatzin's claws —appearing on the second and third "fingers" of an ancient reptilian "hand"—are sharply curved. They drop off when the bird's wing feathers grow in. But even in adulthood the hoatzin is a poor flier; its flights are seldom more than a hundred yards and usually end in a clumsy crash landing.

A BABY HOATZIN flails upside down in the attempt to hook its wing claws onto a branch. It scrambles about in low branches by acrobatics of wings, bill and feet.

GAINING A WING-HOLD, the hoatzin manages to right itself. One of its curved wing claws is clearly visible hooked on the branch at upper right in this picture.

THE RHINOCEROS IGUANA, a fierce-looking but harmless five-foot lizard, haunts the shores of Hispaniola's salt lakes, once a Pleistocene sea channel. There it digs burrows up to 40 feet long in fossil corals.

6

Reptiles and Amphibians

S AY "tropics" to many people, and they immediately conjure up images of snakes, lizards, frogs and crocodiles lurking menacingly in deep, dark rivers. The fact of the matter is that reptiles and amphibians are almost inevitably linked in our minds with the warm, moist lands of the Tropic Zone—and with good reason. There are probably more of these creatures in tropical areas than in any of the other life zones on earth, and this in turn is the result of a simple anatomical difference between reptiles, amphibians and the other vertebrate groups: they are what we call cold-blooded.

The main thing to know about cold-bloodedness is not that the blood runs cold, but that the animal concerned has no internal mechanism for regulating its body heat. Mammals and birds can endure considerable outside temperature changes because they have adaptations enabling them to regulate their own internal temperatures. Reptiles and amphibians, by contrast, must seek outside temperatures which are comfortable to them—and since they, like most animals, function best when they are warm, and the tropics are the warmest areas on our planet, it follows quite logically that a great many of them should be living and evolving there.

The reptilian class includes crocodilians, snakes, lizards and turtles (plus, of course, that rare and very local creature, New Zealand's tuatara). The class Amphibia includes frogs, toads, salamanders and the legless caecilians. In terms of the history of life, amphibians are the oldest vertebrates to live even in part on land, with reptiles developing later and birds and mammals later still. This makes the amphibians interesting historically as well as for the role they play in the natural scheme of things today.

Amphibians differ from reptiles in certain significant ways, all of them indicating greater historical age and hence a closer affinity to their aquatic ancestors. There is usually a young stage, the tadpole or larva, equipped with gills and adapted to life in the water. The skin of amphibians is moist and without scales in most species. Reptiles by contrast are more completely adapted to life on land: their skin is usually dry, with scales, and they have no aquatic stage at any point in their development.

A WARM temperature is not the only factor making the tropics a preferred climate for reptiles and amphibians; an even range of temperature is fully as important. This is found most ideally in the tropical rain forest, where the mean annual temperature is between 75° and 79°F. In this favorable environment, with food of all kinds abundant in the form of plants and insects, both types of animals abound. But above all it is the snakes which flourish in the tropics of the world, and they range in size and variety from minute insect-eaters to enormous hunters of warm-blooded prey.

Yet for all of this abundance, the ordinary visitor to the tropics is not likely ever to see a snake in the course of his everyday activities. Even professional collectors have trouble finding them. A herpetologist friend of mine spent several months on the Peruvian Amazon collecting reptiles and amphibians. He tells me that he would find, on the average, one snake a day—but that almost always each day's snake would be a different species!

This elusiveness of the tropical snakes makes it difficult to quote statistics on their numbers in relation to snake populations elsewhere. They are easier to find in the northern woods than in the tropical rain forest, but this does not mean that they are more abundant there. The rain forest has many more hiding places, and snakes, like other animals, have taken in numbers to life in the treetops, radiating into a great many forms there and occupying niches that are not ordinarily penetrated by man. Even in terms of species it is difficult, in the present state of our knowledge, to make comparisons between South America and other continents. It is clear, however, that tropical America has a lot of snakes, from Mexico right on down through the various habitats of the continent, and that among them are some of the most interesting varieties known.

There are, for example, the boas, anacondas and their smaller relatives. These are primarily American and include, in the anacondas, the largest snakes in the world—their closest rivals are the pythons of the Orient. The greatest recorded length for an anaconda is 37.5 feet, four and a half feet longer than the largest python, and the anacondas are bulkier, weighing considerably more per foot of length.

Anacondas are always found closely associated with water, and so it is natural that the great basin of the Orinoco and Amazon river systems should be their characteristic home. They are frequently found coiled in trees from which they loop down on their prey, but being excellent swimmers, they often strike from the water too. Like the other boas and the pythons, they kill by constriction,

AN ARBOREAL EYE

Among colubrid snakes, there are a few tree-dwelling species with unusually large, bulging eyes which enable them to see in every direction (shown by shaded disks above) without turning their heads. There is even a groove along the snout to facilitate looking straight ahead. This panoramic vision is particularly useful for pursuit of small frogs and lizards in the trees. The eyesight of these snakes is so sharp that they can detect well-camouflaged prey even after it stops moving.

tightening the coils which they throw rapidly around their victims. Death is apparently caused not by crushing, as was thought for so long, but by suffocation and cutting off the blood circulation.

Anacondas live on mammals, birds and the alligatorlike caimans of the rivers. A large anaconda is perfectly capable of swallowing a small calf—I once came across one in the process of digesting a calf it had recently taken. They certainly would be able to swallow a child or even an adult man, but there are very few well-authenticated accounts of attacks on human beings. One would think that anacondas would be feared as among the most dangerous of animals in the regions where they occur, but they are never so considered. Someone has suggested that perhaps a man, walking upright, simply looks too big to be considered prey, and hence attacks on man are few.

Perhaps even more notorious than the anacondas, though often overrated as to size, are their relatives the boas. These are still big snakes, the record length for a boa constrictor being 18.5 feet, but actually specimens over 10 feet long are rare. They are not poisonous, but they do bite on occasion—for example, when captured—and some may continue to be vicious for years in captivity. On the other hand, in some areas of tropical America, they are practically domesticated, being kept around houses to serve the useful function of holding down the populations of such pests as rats.

The best known of the boas is the boa constrictor, which ranges from northern Mexico to Paraguay and northern Argentina. There are, however, many other species, many of them handsomely colored and adapted to arboreal life. The emerald tree boa of Brazil and the Guianas is a striking example. The brilliant green of its body serves for concealment in the forest foliage, and the strongly prehensile tail gives the snake firm anchorage in the treetops. It feeds largely on birds and lizards. There are also boas in the West Indies. They range in size from a little over a foot to as much as 11 feet and have beautifully colored, iridescent skin.

THE majority of snakes everywhere, except in Australia, belong to the family Colubridae. The colubrids are numerous in tropical America and they have adapted to all of the different ways of life, except marine, that are open to snakes. There are extremely slender arboreal forms that slither among the branches with extraordinary ease, like the vine snake *Oxybelis*. There is also a multiformity of ground-living types, and there are some that burrow into the soil, and some that are aquatic.

With all these diverse radiations, the colubrids show a considerable variety of food habits. Like all snakes, they are carnivorous, but many have developed special food-getting adaptations, such as the Dipsadinae, which eat snails. One genus, *Dipsas*, manages this by inserting the lower jaw into the snail's shell and pulling the snail out with its elongate front teeth, like a gourmet picking out his escargots. There are also types that feed on other snakes, and aquatic forms that live on fish. Some of the colubrids have poison glands that open onto teeth at the rear of the mouth, but none of the South American species are considered to be dangerous to man.

The truly poisonous American snakes, aside from a single species of sea snake, all belong to two families, the Elapidae and the Viperidae. The elapids include the cobras and mambas and their relatives of the Old World, and the very different-looking coral snakes of the New World. One species of coral snake occurs in the southeastern United States and another in the southwest, but in Central

FANGS AGAINST FEATHERS

Anchored to a branch by its prehensile tail, the emerald tree boa (above) strikes at a black-breasted puffbird. Long front fangs can easily penetrate the feathers and hold the bird while the snake throws two or three coils around it and then kills it by constriction. On a two-inch skull of the tree boa (below, left) the fangs are often two fifths of an inch long. By contrast, the skull of the boa constrictor (right), which eats more mammals than birds, has fairly even rows of sharp teeth.

and South America about 50 species have been described. Mostly they are small snakes, though one Brazilian species reaches a length of five feet. They are generally brightly colored, most often with rings of red, black and yellow, and have aptly been called "candystick snakes."

A number of different nonpoisonous snakes show candystick colors very similar to those of the coral snake. This may well be a case of mimicry—when we come to discuss tropical American butterflies, for instance, we will see how many harmless kinds take on the shape and colors of poisonous or bad-tasting types—but students of the subject are not yet in agreement about whether this is true of snakes as well.

Coral snakes have a very powerful venom, but because of their secretive habits and unaggressive ways, there are relatively few instances of humans being bitten. However, anyone meeting a coral snake, or handling one, should be extremely careful.

THE most dangerous snakes of tropical America are all members of the viper family. They belong to the subfamily of pit vipers, so named because they have sensory pits on each side of the head. These pits have been shown to be very sophisticated heat detectors which serve to guide the snakes accurately in striking at warm-blooded prey even in total darkness.

The pit vipers include the rattlesnakes, moccasins and copperheads of North America, as well as a number of Eurasian and tropical American species. Their curious distribution has led to some interesting speculation on their history, and though there is little to go on in the form of fossil records, we can do some educated guessing. Thus we might say it appears that these snakes evolved first in Eurasia, reaching North America long enough ago to allow for the development of the rattlesnake group (unknown in the Old World) but not getting to South America until after the establishment of the Pliocene land connection with North America. The pit vipers, then, the most notorious of the Neotropical snakes, belong among the animals that are newcomers to the continent.

The most abundant and widely distributed of the pit vipers is *Bothrops atrox*, which occurs from northeastern Mexico to Peru and all across northern South America. This species, commonly called the fer-de-lance, got its graphic French name, which evokes the image of a spearhead striking, from the settlers on Martinique, where it was common—the only poisonous snake in the West Indies. Related snakes in Brazil are called jararacas, a name derived from Tupi Indian dialect, which can be translated as "Lord of the forest."

There are two dozen or so species of *Bothrops* in tropical America. Most of them are rather small; the fer-de-lance is the largest, usually running four to five feet long, although a maximum length of over eight feet has been reported. Like the rattlesnakes, they give birth to living young and are extremely prolific, producing litters of 60 to 70 snakes at a time. The baby snakes, about a foot long at birth, are active and venomous from the start.

The jararaca is very difficult to see, since its light diamond markings on a brownish or grayish ground color blend perfectly with the leaf litter of the forest floor. Fortunately, these are not aggressive snakes; they usually strike only on provocation. None of the famous naturalists exploring South America has been bitten, though several have had narrow escapes. Henry Walter Bates, the great 19th Century naturalist, reported an incident in which one of his guides came close to treading on a jararaca, which incidentally gives an excellent description of the snake in its habitat. "The individual seen by Lino," he wrote, "lay coiled up at the foot of a tree, and was scarcely distinguishable, on account of the colours of its body being assimilated to those of the fallen leaves. Its hideous, flat triangular head, connected with the body by a thin neck, was reared and turned toward us: Frazaõ killed it with a charge of shot, shattering it completely, and destroying, to my regret, its value as a specimen. In conversing on the subject of Jararácas as we walked onwards, every one of the party was ready to swear that this snake attacks man without provocation, leaping towards him from a considerable distance when he approaches. I met, in the course of my daily rambles in the woods, many Jararácas, and once or twice very narrowly escaped treading on them, but never saw them attempt to spring. On some subjects the testimony of the natives of a wild country is utterly worthless. The bite of the Jararácas is generally fatal. I knew of four or five instances of death from it, and only one clear case of recovery after being bitten; but in that case the person was lamed for life."

Several small species of *Bothrops* are arboreal, with variegated green coloration to blend with foliage, and strongly prehensile tails to help them get about. These are particularly common in Central America and in the forests of the Andes, and are a source of concern for coffee pickers in the plantations of those regions. They are hard to see, and in areas where they occur, one is always acutely conscious of them in pushing through undergrowth.

The bushmaster, largest of the American poisonous snakes, is classified in a separate genus, *Lachesis*, appropriately named for one of the Greek Fates—the one who assigned the length of life to individual human beings. Bushmasters are more slender snakes than fer-de-lances or jararacas, but specimens 12 feet long have been reported. Fortunately, they are rarely encountered by man; their normal prey is small mammals. They lay eggs rather than giving birth to live young and are said to incubate the eggs in their coils.

Curiously, there is only one species of rattlesnake on the mainland of South America, though there are something like 25 species in Mexico and the United States. Obviously most of the rattlesnakes did not take to the South American environment when the land connection was formed. The single tropical rattlesnake species, however, ranges from Mexico to Argentina, and it is often abundant in savanna country. The South American rattler has a particularly powerful venom that acts primarily on the nervous system, causing rapid paralysis (North American rattlesnake poison, by contrast, acts mainly on the circulatory system, dissolving red corpuscles in the blood).

S NAKES are dramatic creatures; turtles are less so, but the predominant turtles of South America have characteristics of great interest to zoologists. One family, for instance, the Chelidae, or snake-necked turtles, is found only in South America, Australia and New Guinea. Another family, the Pelomedusidae, or hidden-necked turtles, occurs only in South America, Africa and Madagascar. Both these families in former times were evidently dispersed throughout the northern continents but have now become extinct there. Thus they appear to be among the oldtimers in South America, differing from the animals familiar in North America and Europe in that they conceal the head beneath the shell by bending the neck sideways instead of pulling it in.

Perhaps the most interesting turtle is a river species named *Podocnemis expansa*, which has long been of great importance in the lives of the peoples of the Amazon and Orinoco drainage systems. This is the largest of the fresh-water turtles, weighing up to 150 pounds or more, with a shell as much as three feet long and two feet wide. But its importance to human populations where it lives is due more to its numbers than to size.

At the height of the dry season, when the rivers are at their lowest levels, the turtles come out of the water to lay their eggs on sand bars—from January until March along the Orinoco, in August or September on the upper Amazon. Great crowds of them crawl onto the land in the early hours of the morning to dig their nests. This is the time the local people wait for eagerly. The turtles are extremely shy, so easily disturbed by sound or movement that different villages habitually post guards on nearby sand bars to be sure that the turtles will not be frightened into other territories.

BATES, Humboldt and other naturalists have described the egg harvest. Notices were posted on church doors announcing the date, and the entire population of a village would descend on a sand bar, which was divided up carefully among the different household groups. "It was," wrote Bates, "an animating sight to behold the wide circle of rival diggers throwing up clouds of sand in their energetic labours, and working gradually toward the centre of the ring. . . . By the end of the second day . . . large mounds of eggs, some of them four to five feet in height, were then seen by the side of each hut, the produce of the labours of the family."

The eggs were used chiefly for the production of oil, which served for cooking, lighting and other purposes. The usual method of extracting the oil was to pile eggs in an empty canoe, mash them, pour water over them, and then skim off the oil which rose to the surface after the canoe had been sitting in the warm sun for a few hours. Bates calculated that about 8,000 jars of oil, each holding three gallons, were produced annually on the upper Amazon. Since it took about 6,000 eggs to make three gallons of oil, he figured that 48 million eggs were destroyed each year—the product of 400,000 turtles. Many egg nests, of course, escaped discovery; but the newly hatched turtles were considered a great delicacy, and many thousands more were destroyed by people lying in wait for

WALKING ON THE WATER

Despite their frightening appearance, the crested basilisks are harmless lizards that feed on insects and plants. The two-foot-long common basilisk shown here lives along the banks of Central American streams. Ordinarily quadrupedal, it is also adept at bipedal locomotion and often escapes danger by rearing up and racing for water, where it skims the surface for several yards before sinking in and swimming away. This feat is made possible partly by the speed of the animal and the surface tension of the water, and partly by its long widespread hind toes, which are fringed with tiny scales giving additional support.

them as they hatched and set out on their hazardous journey to the water.

Turtle meat was a staple article of diet for people living near the rivers. "Every house," Bates noted, "has a little pond, called a curral (pen), in the backyard to hold a stock of the animals through the season of dearth. . . . I became so sick of turtle in the course of two years," he added, "that I could not bear the smell of it, although at the same time nothing else was to be had, and I was suffering actual hunger."

Among the enemies of the turtles, aside from men, are the crocodiles and caimans of the rivers. There are only two true crocodiles in South America: the Orinoco crocodile, which is found only in that river system; and the American crocodile, which ranges from the southern tip of Florida to northern South America and, like some of its Old World relatives, seems equally at home in salt water and in fresh. There are seven species of caimans, usually classified in three genera; they are entirely Neotropical and are more like alligators than crocodiles, differing from alligators only in minor details of anatomy. In fact, most of the "alligators" sold in pet shops in the United States are actually caimans, since true alligators are so well protected by law in America that live specimens are very hard to obtain.

THE Orinoco crocodile is the largest of its kind in the New World. Alexander von Humboldt, exploring the Orinoco early in the 19th Century, found individuals 20 to 24 feet long—by comparison, the largest then recorded specimen of the American alligator measured 19 feet, 2 inches. The black caiman of the Amazon attains a maximum length of 15 feet, though most caimans are smaller, averaging between five and seven feet long. The caimans have been so thoroughly hunted for their hides in the present century that large specimens are rarely seen, and even small ones are far less numerous than they once were.

Naturalists of the last century were impressed by the incredible abundance of caimans in the rivers. Bates wrote that "it is scarcely exaggerating to say that the waters of the Solimoens are as well stocked with large alligators in the dry

season, as a ditch in England is in summer with tadpoles." And Humboldt on the Orinoco said "they swarm like worms in the shallow waters of the river." But these swarms have now mostly been converted into shoes and belts and pocketbooks, products of a lively industry in caiman hides.

Few people lament the reduction in numbers of crocodiles and caimans—though perhaps more should, since in some areas they have been brought close to extinction. The South American reptiles are not really man-eaters; they simply eat anything they can catch and kill, which sometimes includes people and even each other. They are generally hated and feared, and all of the explorers have reports of deaths which they consider reliable, and in some cases they were witnesses of accidents. Alfred Russel Wallace wrote that "in almost every village some persons may be seen maimed by these creatures and many children are killed every year." As with poisonous snakes, none of the explorers themselves became a victim, perhaps because they were always aware of the danger and correspondingly cautious.

THE present caimans are descendants of oldtimers on the continent, and so are most of the South American lizards. The majority of the lizards of both North and South America belong to a family, the Iguanidae, that is found only in the New World—except for two genera in Madagascar and one in the Fiji and Tonga Islands of the Pacific. These latter clearly are relicts, left over from some ancient time when iguanids were widely distributed; but why the family should have failed in the Old World and been so successful in the New is one of the mysteries of evolution.

Like so many of the other special Neotropical animal groups, the iguanids have adapted to a wide variety of ecological niches. They range from southern Canada to the tip of the South American mainland, and from the seacoast to the high paramo zone of the Andes. They have evolved diverse forms, from the horned toads of North American deserts to the slender and agile anoles and the large ungainly iguanas themselves. There are about 165 species of anoles, ranging from southern Virginia to southern Brazil. Some of them are called "chameleons" because of their ability to change color, though they are quite unrelated to the true chameleons of the Old World. Most commonly they change from green to brown depending on their mood, but other colors—blues, oranges, reds and yellows—may be involved as well. In tropical America there is almost always some species or other of iguanid making itself at home around houses and gardens. They are among animals that get along nicely with man. In the forest the different species tend to be restricted to particular levels—the ground, tree trunks, low branches or the high canopy.

There are many kinds of lizards in the forest, but among the most curious are the basilisks, named for ferocious mythological monsters of old. The small basilisks, at most two feet or so long, look fierce enough, especially the adult males with great crests on their heads and down their backs; but they are really timid, at least in the face of so large a creature as man. Some basilisks live near water courses, and when alarmed take to the water, not swimming but actually skittering along on their long-toed hind feet over the surface as long as they can keep up speed. In Spanish they are often called Jesús Cristo because of this ability.

Iguanas in the narrow sense, species of the genus *Iguana*, are also usually found near water and swim easily—they are too big and heavy to have the basilisk ability to run over the water surface. They are expert climbers and are all herbivorous as adults (the young also eat insects), eating leaves, flowers, seed pods and the like. The largest and best-known species, *Iguana iguana*, may reach a total length of over six feet. This, to be sure, is mostly tail, but the animal still seems very much a fierce-looking, miniature dragon, though in reality it is timid. Iguanas are known for their habit of dropping off branches of high trees in the gallery forest, crashing downward from branch to branch and finishing up, in the water at last, with a tremendous splash. The effect of this can be quite startling, particularly when one is in a canoe turning a bend in a river.

Iguanas are highly prized as food everywhere in tropical America, and live ones can almost always be found in the markets. The flesh has a delicate, chickenlike quality and flavor which anyone must admit to be tasty, unless prejudiced against the idea of eating lizards. I remember a dinner party at which we served iguanas, thinking that everyone understood what a delicacy they were eating. One of the guests, a French lady, had missed the point, however; when she at last realized it was a lizard that she had been eating so happily, she became physically ill. Why should some people regard the eating of lizards with such intolerant horror, and at the same time unhesitatingly accept frog legs as a delicacy?

Frogs, of course, are not reptiles, but amphibians. The class Amphibia in South America has surprises both for the layman and the scientist. Salamanders, for example, are common enough animals in the North Temperate Zone of Eurasia and North America, although they are a much less conspicuous element in the South American fauna. Eighteen species are known there, but six of these were not described scientifically until 1963.

They have not been much noticed because they are such small and unobtrusive animals. Some of them, furthermore, have picked really out-of-the-way habitats, like the species that live high in the trees in their own little ponds of rain water collected by bromeliad plants. The obscure, wormlike animals called caecilians, on the other hand, are represented by some 40 species.

Frogs and toads, too, although familiar and numerous in North America and Europe, are represented by far fewer species as compared with the tropics. In North America for instance, there are 12 species in the state of Michigan, while the tiny country of Costa Rica, with slightly more than half the land area of Michigan, has about 130 species.

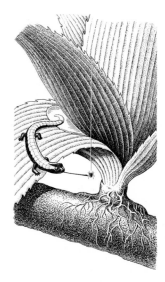

A WATERY RETREAT

Like other amphibians, which have thin, porous skins, salamanders require moist surroundings. The Mexican flat-toed salamander, an eight-inch-long arboreal species with webbed feet, is shown here on the cuplike base of a bromeliad brimming with rain water. On the leaves unfurling from this natural reservoir, which is often high above the ground, live the small insects and spiders on which the salamander feeds. Throughout the dry season, when bromeliads provide moist refuges in the trees, the salamander lives in one or two of the plants, but at other times of the year it wanders freely.

THE ancestral amphibians were the first of the vertebrates to come out on land, far back in the Devonian period. These were of types long since extinct: but the frogs, even though they do not go back to the Devonian, have a very ancient lineage and have gone through many vicissitudes in the course of their long geological history, so that the living groups, the kinds that have happened to survive into the present, often have oddly discontinuous distributions. Thus the leptodactylid frogs, like the marsupials among the mammals, are found only in America and in the Australasian region. They are, however, far more numerous and varied in South America than in Australia, with 25 or 30 genera and hundreds of species as against only 16 genera and 62 species in the Australasian region.

Another frog family, the Pipidae, is found only in South America and in Africa. These curious frogs have no tongues. They depend entirely on their long, slender fingers to get food—in the case of the Surinam toad (*Pipa pipa*), for example, any moving object which touches the fingers is swept into the mouth by reflex action. (One of the African tongueless frogs, *Xenopus*, acquired fame a generation ago when it was discovered that it would start to lay eggs a few hours after being injected with urine from a pregnant human female, providing a rapid test for pregnancy. Other pregnancy tests, however, have now dimmed exotic *Xenopus'* fame.)

Another celebrated South American amphibian is the "giant toad," or "poisonous toad," *Bufo marinus*, and its related species. Adults of this large toad may weigh as much as five pounds, and they have voracious appetites for all sorts of insects. They are tough, hardy and prolific, a single female laying as many as 32,000 eggs. They have been introduced into the West Indies, Bermuda, Hawaii and other Pacific islands where native predators are scarce, as an aid in controlling insects in cane fields, gardens and the like. It is not their bite that is poisonous, but two large glands on the back of the neck which produce a milky, toxic secretion. It probably tastes bad, too, because the animals are left strictly alone by their natural predators.

A VORACIOUS FROG

No timid creatures, South America's horned frogs even prey on animals as large as themselves—lying in wait for them, leaping out at them as they pass by and snapping them up in their huge mouths. Shown above is a five-inch-long Wied's frog feasting on a young web-footed rat. Unable to swallow the rat whole, the frog will digest it gradually. Preyed on in turn by other animals, such frogs may gain a measure of protection from their horns, which, though no more than flaps of skin, look formidable and make their wide heads seem wider still.

A LARGE number of kinds of frogs of several families have taken to the trees in South America. One important problem for such arboreal frogs is metamorphosis—how to manage the tadpole stage in water. Several different solutions have been found for this. Some come down to the ground to lay eggs in water like any normal frog. Others plaster the eggs on leaves in places where the tadpoles will fall into the water when they hatch. A few, like the salamander, take advantage of the water collected in the "tanks" of bromeliads. For *Dendrobates* and *Phyllobates* trees are only an occasional refuge. The male, who stays near the eggs until they hatch, carries the tadpoles to water on his back, sometimes seeking it out in holes in trunks or branches.

But in the case of the Surinam toad, the female winds up holding the eggs. When she is ready to lay, she is clasped firmly by a male and the pair remains together for more than a day. As the eggs come out of the oviduct, the female starts a forward somersault, and the eggs slide into flaps of skin on the male's belly. As the somersault is completed, they drop out again onto the female's back, which consists of rather spongy tissue. The male presses the eggs into this soft tissue and fertilizes them. From 40 to more than 200 eggs are thus implanted, to remain on the back of the female throughout their development until the young are ready to emerge as tiny, fully formed froglets.

The British naturalist Gerald Durrell found several of these frogs while collecting animals in British Guiana. The young started to emerge on the ship voyage home and Durrell, in his book *Three Tickets to Adventure*, described the birth of them thus:

"In one of the pockets I could see the tiny occupant twitching and struggling frantically, turning round and round, so that first its legs and then its head appeared in the opening. Then it remained quiet for some time. Having rested, it proceeded to thrust its head and shoulders through the opening. Then it paused again to rest, for it seemed to be a considerable effort to prise itself loose from the encircling rim of its mother's thick, elastic skin. Presently it started to wriggle like a fish, throwing its head from side to side, and slowly its body started to ease itself out of the pocket, like a reluctant cork out of a bottle. Soon it was lying exhausted across its mother's back, with only its hind feet still hidden inside the pockmark that had been its nursery for so long. Then it dragged itself across its mother's cratered and eroded skin, slid into the water, and floated immobile, another scrap of life entering the universe."

NEWLY SPRUNG FROM A POUCH ON ITS MOTHER'S BACK, A GREAT GRAY MARSUPIAL TREE FROGLET LOOKS BEFORE IT LEAPS INTO THE WORLD

Land of the Cold-blooded

The hot jungle of tropical America is alive with reptiles and amphibians. In the rivers of the continent swim the caiman and the largest of all snakes, the anaconda. The shady interior of the forest conceals numerous tree snakes. Tiny frogs swarm in the foliage, and the lush carpet of undergrowth is the home of a unique, beautifully marked frog family, most of whose members are poisonous.

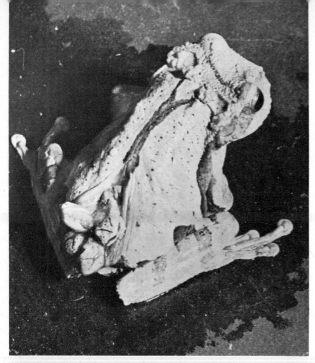

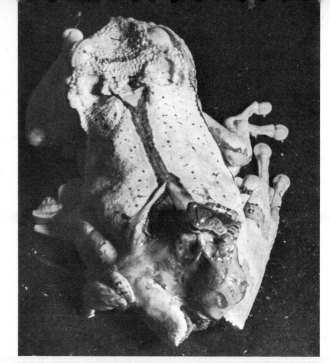

AS BIRTH BEGINS, THE MARSUPIAL FROG'S "ZIPPER" OPENS WIDE

TWO DEEP IN A BULGING POUCH, FROGLETS PUSH EACH OTHER OUT

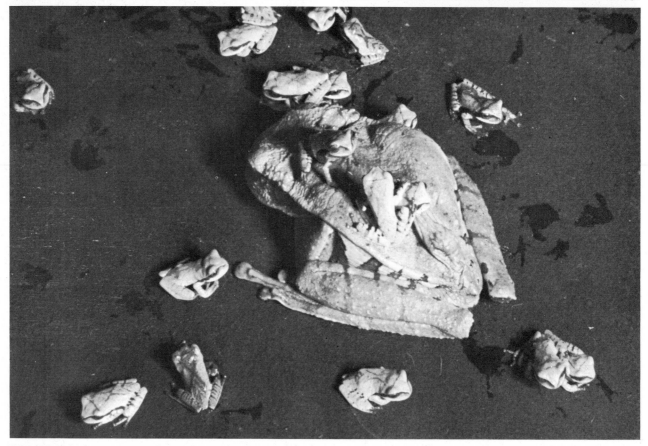

THE LAST OF 21 BABIES EMERGES FROM THE POUCH AS EARLIER ARRIVALS HOP IN ALL DIRECTIONS AND THE EXHAUSTED MOTHER SLUMPS

From Egg to Frog— without Water

Most frogs hatch out as tadpoles in ponds, puddles or streams. There, with tail fins and gills, they gradually mature to frogs, a process recalling the evolution from fish to amphibians some 365 million years ago. Not so the great gray marsupial frog. On the steep Venezuelan mountainsides where it lives,

A Y-SHAPED FURROW, OR "ZIPPER," DIVIDES THE MARSUPIAL FROG'S POUCH; THE MALE MAY HELP TO PLACE THE FERTILIZED EGGS INSIDE

there is practically no still water available. Torrential rains sluice away or sink into the mossy jungle floor. To make up for the dearth of pools, the female frog must provide for her eggs in some other way. Eggs develop and hatch in a pouch on the back, secured by a "zipper." Here the tadpoles are incubated—nourished by yolks and completely wrapped up in their overgrown gills. When the pouch unzips, fully formed froglets pop out. Within 10 seconds after birth, they are agile enough to jump over the mother's back, and when eight hours old, will try to capture big moths, on which the adults feed.

COCHRANELLA, a three-quarter-inch tree frog, crouches on a leaf over a stream. Here the female will deposit her eggs.

THE EGG MASS is attached to the underside of the leaf, insuring that the hatching tadpoles fall directly into the water.

Other Egg and Tadpole Oddities

The great gray marsupial frog is not the only one to have departed from the usual amphibian life cycle. The strange breeding habits of many other tropical American frogs are added proof of an evolutionary trend away from development in the water. Instead of spawning many small eggs in a pond or river, some frogs deposit their eggs in bromeliad water tanks up in trees. Others stick them to leaves or branches directly over the water so that tadpoles drop in on hatching. Sometimes the males carry the tadpoles on their backs to tree hollows filled with rain water. All of these practices cut down on the time spent as defenseless eggs or tadpoles in waters that teem with hungry predators. As a result these frogs can make do with fewer eggs and thus spawn larger ones, which supply more yolk for each developing embryo.

EGGS ON HER BACK are the responsibility of a female *Cerathyla*. Many other tree frogs care for their eggs in this manner, carrying them about while they develop and finally dropping them in the water-filled cup of a bromeliad for only a few days of tadpole life.

TADPOLES ON HIS BACK, up to 15 of them, are borne by a male kokoi. He keeps an eye on the eggs, which are spawned on land, and is standing by when they hatch so that the baby tadpoles can wriggle onto his back and glue themselves there. They are kept moist by periodic dunking, but if any should fall off before growing very much bigger, they cannot survive.

Beautiful but Deadly

Being small, soft-bodied and succulent, frogs are heavily preyed upon, and it is remarkable that so many survive. One reason is that many of them are so artfully colored in various shades of green and brown that they are almost invisible against a background of leaves or reeds so long as they hold still. Therefore it seems incongruous indeed that many tropical frogs should be brilliantly colored—until it is discovered that they are also poisonous. Their colors are believed to be advertisements, so that predatory animals will immediately recognize and avoid touching or eating them.

The frogs shown below are only four of the 20 or so known poisonous species in tropical America, and there may well be many others, since most of them occur in dense rain forest areas that have been little explored and in which little collecting has been done. The men who know these frogs the best are the various Indian tribesmen of Central and South America. They have long been aware of the extreme toxicity of these animals and have learned how to toast them to bring out the virulence of the poison in their skins, which is then smeared on the tips of blowgun darts or arrowheads. One frog provides enough poison to treat 30 to 50 such weapons.

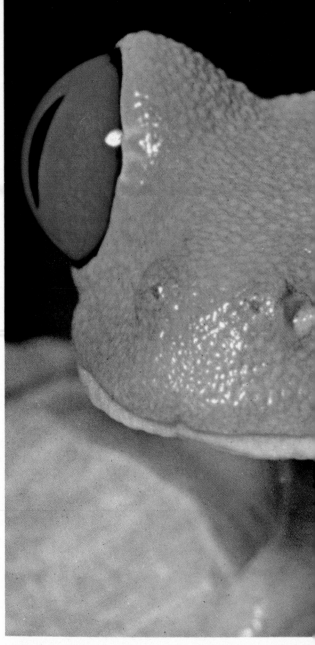

THANKS TO ITS BRIGHT GREEN SKIN, THE NONPOISONOUS RED-EYED

BRILLIANT WARNING COLORS advertise the hazards of molesting four frogs of the *Dendrobates* genus, all of whose members are poisonous. These frogs are active in the daytime and

conspicuous by nature. Their venom is located in glands in the skin and is released on contact, attacking the neuromuscular apparatus of an enemy via the bloodstream. As a conse-

...OG OF CENTRAL AMERICA BLENDS WELL INTO FOLIAGE. ONLY ITS EYES BETRAY IT, BUT THEY ARE SELDOM SEEN, AS THE FROG IS NOCTURNAL

quence, Indians use leaves as a precaution when they are handling *Dendrobates*, to make sure that they are not poisoned through cuts or scratches on their hands. If through careless- ness they are, the result is a painful local irritation. Far more lethal is cooked and dried skin stuck to darts. Used in hunt- ing, a treated dart totally paralyzes a deer in a few minutes.

THREADING A SINUOUS PATH through the hanging fruits of a palm, the vine snake *Oxybelis* is about 160 times longer than its greatest width. It can bridge wide gaps between boughs, and passes through curtains of tropical foliage smoothly and noiselessly. When motionless or gently swaying, it resembles one of the lianas which festoon the trees of the rain forest.

DISGUISED IN WARNING COLORS, the "two headed" false coral snake is actually harmless. When threatened, it rears both head and tail, and thus sometimes confuses an attacker.

The Way of the Serpent

Like snakes everywhere, those of the American tropics have adopted ways of life that reflect their surroundings. Because of the thickness of the foliage and because so many other creatures inhabit trees, many snakes also live there, the small ones preying on insects and frogs, the larger ones on birds, bats and monkeys.

Tree snakes have evolved in two very different directions. Some are slender colubrids that depend on concealment, twining and slithering like ribbons in the greenery. A few of these, like the one at left, are poisonous. They have fangs in the rear of their mouths, and by holding and chewing a lizard, can paralyze it in a minute or so. By contrast, the boas (*right*) are a nonpoisonous family of powerful constrictors that suffocate their prey with tight coils thrown around its body. Most boas are under 10 feet, but the boa constrictor and the still larger anaconda, a river snake, may run twice that size.

DEFTLY COILED in the branches, the emerald tree boa (*top*) holds on with its prehensile tail, a climbing aid also possessed by the Cook's (*center*) and the garden tree boa (*bottom*).

143

CAUGHT IN THE COILS of a 19-foot anaconda, a seven-and-a-half foot caiman on the bank of the Coeswijne River in Surinam is doomed to suffocation, despite its sharp teeth and scaly armor. Anacondas often lurk in the water, to entangle and drown prey. To balance matters, young anacondas, just over two feet long at birth, are also eaten by large caimans.

The Gigantic Anaconda

Largest of all living snakes, the anaconda is the Spirit of the Amazon, haunting the dark pools of swamps and tributaries, with eyes "as big as the full moon." The Indians believe that anyone swallowed by the Spirit lives forever inside its body, unharmed. In northern South America, this legendary snake may be truly gigantic, growing to a record length of 37.5 feet and capable of swallowing a 150-pound animal. But most of the larger specimens measure about 18 feet and weigh up to 200 pounds. Anacondas of this size are the natural predators of the alligatorlike caimans of the rivers. More usual prey, however, are the water birds, and semiaquatic mammals such as the capybaras, which are plentiful and easy to catch.

Unless extremely hungry or provoked in some way, anacondas seldom attack people. The few recorded deaths all occurred in water. No one knows the hazards of such an encounter better than Mike Tsalikis, a professional hunter and dealer in wild animals, whose memorable experience with an 18-footer is pictured here and on the following pages.

HUNTING ANACONDAS IN COLOMBIA, Mike Tsalikis paddles toward the sunlit fallen tree where his helpers have located an 18-foot specimen. It is draped over the trunk to sleep.

DISTURBED BY THE CANOE'S APPROACH, the anaconda is quick to head for water, where it can swim to safety. But the hunter is close enough to reach out and grab its neck with both hands. The struggle overturns the boat, and Tsalikis is thrown into the shallows. Immediately the snake's muscular body, almost as thick as a telephone pole, begins to coil around him.

145

The Anaconda Caught

Hunters who supply zoos, laboratories and film makers with live anacondas usually try to find individuals that have taken to the shore to sun or digest their food. At home in the water, the big reptiles are extremely difficult to catch and even harder to handle. Out of their element, they are slower. Even so, it takes no fewer than two or three men to subdue one, which is firmly anchored on a tree branch. One member of the team climbs up to grab the neck, followed by another who unwraps its body, starting with the tail. The snake is then put in a bag—and crated as an extra precaution.

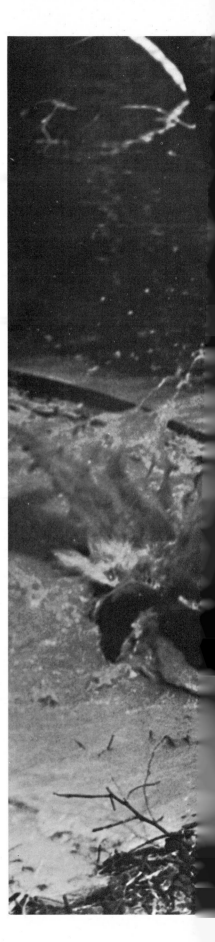

FIGHTING FOR HIS LIFE, snake hunter Mike Tsalikis holds back the anaconda's head to keep from being bitten and drags himself to the edge of the bank. When help arrives (*opposite*), he is almost entirely encoiled, with the snake's tail braced against his chin; within minutes, its squeeze would have been fatal.

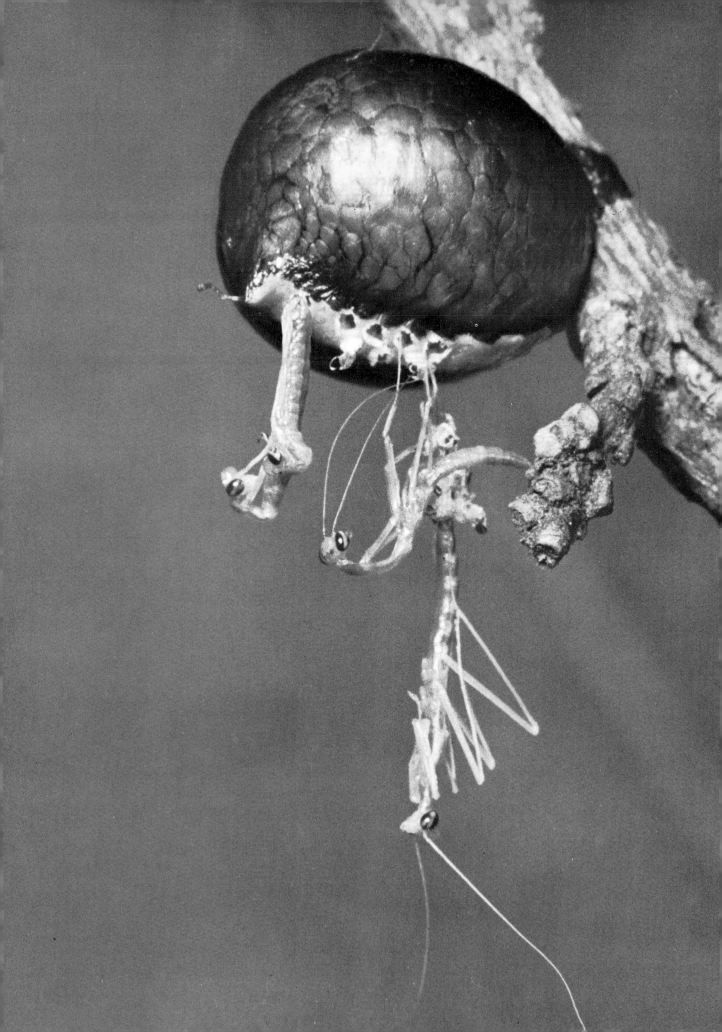

7

The Insect
Legions

IF the space in this book were divided up according to the relative abundance
of animals, we would have started on page 1 with insects and we would still
be discussing them now. For in the world as a whole, there are probably at
least four million species of insects, of which more than 800,000 different kinds
have already been described by entomologists and given technical names—and
in the tropics there are more insects than in any other area on earth. By comparison, the world has only about 4,300 species of mammals, 8,600 species of
birds, some 8,900 amphibians and reptiles, and 5,000 fresh-water fishes. So
when we start looking at insects, we enter a part of the animal kingdom that is
not only crowded with life, but has the added fascination of constant surprise
and discovery as we encounter species we have never met before.

Consider what my co-workers and I learned years ago in the course of our
work at the yellow fever laboratory in Villavicencio in eastern Colombia. We
were interested in studying the mosquitoes which carried the disease in the jungle, and simply in pursuing this research we found 150 species of mosquitoes
within a 10-mile radius of the laboratory. By contrast, there are only about 125
species known for the whole continent of North America north of Mexico! And

yet we were not even trying to collect different species; we were not especially on the lookout for different varieties and had no feeling that our list of mosquito species for the area was anywhere near complete. Which shows why it is so difficult to be positive about insect distribution in the tropics, and why so much remains still to be learned.

Mosquitoes, because of their importance in the transmission of disease, are among the best studied of insects. Something like 1,500 species from different parts of the world have been described, and of these, more than 500 are found in the Neotropical region. This is a considerably larger number than exists in any of the other major faunal regions. Furthermore, the Neotropical mosquitoes are more distinctive than those of any other realm. The mosquitoes of the world, in the most widely used classification, are divided into 88 "subgeneric" groups —and of these, 23 alone are peculiar to the Neotropical region, as compared to 11 in the Australasian region, eight in the Oriental region, and only four in the African realm.

This great number of different kinds of tropical mosquitoes means also great diversity of habits. The mosquito responsible for transmitting yellow fever, for example, was demonstrated by Walter Reed and his colleagues after the Spanish-American War to be *Aedes aegypti*, a species of African origin presumably brought over in the slave ships. In America, this species was found to live always in close association with man, breeding in water in discarded cans, vases, rain barrels and other artificial containers. However, yellow fever also occurred in jungle areas where *Aedes aegypti* was unknown and where man existed only in very few numbers. Obviously, there was another mosquito carrier and another host. Our investigations at the yellow fever laboratory indicated that the most probable carrier was a bright-blue, day-flying mosquito called *Haemagogus capricorni*. Sometimes, however, this species could be found only rarely or not at all in areas where infections were known to have occurred. This led to a whole chain of discoveries of mosquito habits. We noticed, for example, that the mosquitoes suddenly became very abundant just after a tree had been felled. For a while we went around in the forest cutting down trees, always stirring up numbers of our bright-blue quarry. But where were the mosquitoes before the trees were cut? We quickly found the answer by climbing: they were in the treetops. This started an elaborate study of the distribution of different kinds of mosquitoes in the forest. We built ladders and platforms in the trees in selected areas, so that the work could be carried out in relative comfort.

WE eventually learned that each species of mosquito had characteristic flight habits. Some were found only near the ground, others lived mostly in the middle canopy, still others high in the trees. *Haemagogus*, it turned out, was a high-canopy dweller and it finally proved to be the chief carrier of jungle yellow fever. The chief vertebrate hosts, we found, were those other tree dwellers, the monkeys. Thus the regular cycle of the disease was between tree-dwelling mosquitoes and monkeys, and man got infected only more or less by accident. With some good reason we came to call jungle yellow fever "an occupational disease of woodcutters."

It is virtually impossible to reconstruct the geological history of insects. True, many fossils have been discovered, but these are mostly from a few localities where conditions for preservation were particularly favorable. The record is thus very spotty and of little use in explaining the present distribution of various groups. However, we know that the major insect orders are all quite ancient, antedating the isolation of South America as an island continent, so that there has been ample time for the evolution of a local fauna. Consequently, the insects, like other animal groups, must surely include not only oldtimers, but also island-hoppers and newcomers which came across the Panama land bridge from the north.

Best known and most conspicuous are the butterflies and moths—members of the order Lepidoptera. Here South America excels both in number of species and in brilliance of coloring. It was once said that the two American continents had more species of Lepidoptera than all of the rest of the world put together. This is probably not true, because of the host of local forms on the various islands of the East Indies. Nevertheless, South America does have more species than any other single continental area and could as aptly be called "the butterfly continent" as the "bird continent."

In the case of birds, however, it is possible to cite the number of families that are limited to the Neotropical region. When it comes to butterflies, this statistic, unfortunately, is unavailable, at least in any reliable form. There is little agreement among taxonomists about what constitutes a family among the butterflies, and as a result it is virtually impossible to make any kind of local counts. Some systems even classify all butterfly families as cosmopolitan. This may be because butterfly families are larger and more heterogeneous groupings than bird families, or it may simply be because butterfly families were all distinct before South America became an island continent, and hence can be said to have been distributed worldwide.

SPOTS BEFORE THE EYES

Many butterflies and moths owe their lives to eyespots on their hind wings. In the case of the South American hairstreak butterfly (above) the spots serve to distract predators from vital parts, and together with the antennaelike tails may help give the illusion of a second head. The owl-eyed moth (below) uses its spots differently. Hidden while the moth is at rest on a tree, they flash into sight as it flicks open its wings—and startle a predator briefly so that the moth may be able to escape unharmed.

WHATEVER you may call them, "families" or otherwise, it is clear that when it comes to distinctive butterfly types, the Neotropical region has a very considerable number. The first such group that comes to mind is that of the morphoes, the large, brilliant, high-flying species of the rain forest. There are some 50 species here, and in most of them the males are iridescent blue, making dazzling flashes of color as they fly through sunny openings in the canopy, tantalizingly out of reach of the collector's net. The females, as is so often the case with butterflies and birds, are much less conspicuous. The brilliant coloring of the males is not due to pigment but, just as with hummingbirds, is the result of the scattering of light through microscopically thin, transparent films on the scales of the butterfly's wings.

The morphoes are large butterflies, the largest attaining a wingspread of seven inches. Not many of the South American species exceed this, but morphoes are still not giants in their world: the bird-winged butterflies of the East Indies span as much as 10 inches.

Another purely Neotropical group, classified by some as a separate family, is the Brassolidae, or "owl butterflies." The largest of these, species of the genus *Caligo*, are almost as big as morphoes, but their dominant colors are browns or grays, and they tend to live in deep shade. The hind wings have large, eyelike spots on the underside, and mounted specimens, turned upside down with the hind wings forward, do have a strikingly owl-like appearance. This, however, is pure coincidence: in nature the butterflies, flying right side up, do not look owl-like. Among many of these butterflies, the eyespots on the hind wings show even when the wings are folded. These quite clearly serve the function of fooling predators into attacking a nonvital part. The eyespots make the hind wing look like the head, and specimens are often seen with this part of the wing notched out harmlessly from an attack by some lizard or bird.

The *Caligo* and other brassolids tend to be most active early in the morning or toward dusk. Some brassolids even fly at night—an unusual habit for butterflies. We think of butterflies as daytime insects, and of moths as crepuscular, or twilight, fliers; and this is generally true, although actually the differences between them are many and subtle, and depend on no single factor. And in the tropics there are a few butterflies that are crepuscular, and a great many moths that fly only by day. These day-flying moths are particularly numerous in the South American region and they tend to be as brightly colored and beautiful as any butterfly.

The day-flying moths belong to several different families. One of these, the Castniidae, includes rather large and gaudy insects that are much prized by collectors. They are hard to catch because of their rapid, dashing flight and habit of staying high in the forest trees. They are considered to be rather primitive compared with butterflies, probably similar to the type that was anciently ancestral to the butterflies, and they are surely to be listed among the South American "oldtimers." Castniids are found in the tropics of both hemispheres; and while they are most numerous in South America, there are also some species in Australia and New Guinea—another indication of ancient lineage.

OTHER striking day-flying moths belong to the family Uraniidae. These also occur in the tropics of both hemispheres, but the gaudiest species are in South America on the one hand, and in Madagascar (also the home of many ancient animal types) on the other. The Neotropical species of *Urania* look strikingly like swallowtail butterflies: the wings are black, marked with iridescent blue-green bands, and the hind wings have graceful tails.

These uraniids are among the insects that sometimes engage in extraordinary mass movements or migrations. *Urania fulgens* is particularly well known for this because tremendous flights of these moths often take place in the Canal Zone, in full view not only of the local population but also of travelers on ships going through the canal. The flights are most apt to take place in June or July, and sometimes the air will be alive with these bright creatures for several days in succession as they furiously flap their way eastward.

Where are they going, and why? Nobody really knows the answer. Butterfly migrations have been intensively studied for some years now, yet learned speculation is about the best the experts have been able to come up with. In the case of the North American monarch butterfly, it has been quite definitely established that a true migration is undertaken to the south every fall, with the insects returning north in the spring like the birds; but in the tropics, the mass movements often seem to be in one direction only. Darwin, in 1833, reported a mass flight of butterflies which he observed from the deck of the *Beagle* out at sea off the coast of Patagonia: "One evening, when we were about ten miles from the Bay of San Blas, vast numbers of butterflies, in bands or flocks of countless myriads, extended as far as the eye could range. Even by the aid of a telescope it was not possible to see a space free from butterflies. The seamen cried out 'it was snowing butterflies,' and such in fact was the appearance."

Such flights sound quite incredible, like the march of lemmings to the sea, yet there are many reports of them. I myself stood on a beach in Honduras years ago and watched millions of butterflies stream past, heading out to sea. The mass flights—migratory or otherwise—may take any one of several forms: sometimes the insects fly on a wide front, sometimes in a narrow ribbon that takes many hours to pass, sometimes in thin, diffuse groupings, sometimes in clouds, sometimes in swarms. But whatever form the flight may take, the behavior of the individual insect is so characteristic that a lepidopterist can spot a migrating butterfly even if it is separated a considerable distance from its fellows: it shows tendencies described variously as "wild energy" and "an almost mad flight."

It has been theorized that this is indeed mass suicide—"nature's way of dealing with overpopulation"—but if this is so, then why does the habit persist? Why is it not eliminated by natural selection? It seems more likely that swarming is a change in behavior that promotes the survival and dispersal of the species, to which the occasional mass suicide is incidental. The behavioral change provides a way in which the species can occasionally burst out from one kind of habitat into others. It certainly results, in some cases, in a broadening of the ecological food base, should the species succeed in surviving in a new habitat by switching to a new plant food. It gives the species two ways of life—a stay-at-home and a wandering phase—instead of leaving it chained to one, and occasionally it even results in the insects becoming established in new regions. In this connection it is interesting that the species of butterflies and other insects that show these mass movements are apt to be species with wide distributions.

Butterfly migration is difficult to understand—but so are many other things about them. Why are the South American butterflies, like the birds, so numerous in species? And why, in the course of evolution, have they developed characteristics different from those on other continents? Tails on the hind wing, for instance. One group of butterflies is called swallowtails because its members characteristically have tails, though many tropical members of the group have lost them. In South America, however, not only do swallowtails have tails but many other butterfly groups do as well—skippers, metalmarks and several genera of Nymphalidae, the family that includes the majority of common roadside butterflies everywhere. What possible meaning can these tails have?

A considerable number of different Neotropical butterflies have also developed transparent wings. Some experts believe that there is no particular reason for this—that, as occasionally happens in nature, a structure or a function has simply been lost or not developed. Others feel that in species living in the deep forest, the transparency obviously serves for concealment.

An unusual number of Neotropical butterflies belonging to quite unrelated groups have long and narrow forewings and small, rounded hind wings. There is a large genus of African butterflies, *Acraea*, with a similar wing shape, but no other continent has anything like the diversity and number of species with this peculiar form. Most numerous are the heliconiids and ithomiids, both groups found only in the New World. *Heliconius* is a very large genus, with something like 70 species (each has many varieties; *H. melopomene*, for instance, has 54 named forms). For the most part, these butterflies are black with bold markings of yellow, red or blue, which make them extremely conspicuous insects. Their bright colors and slow, leisurely flight make them seem indifferent to possible attack by insect-eating enemies. And it turns out that indeed they are immune to attack because of acrid body juices that make them distasteful if not actually poisonous. The varied and numerous species of ithomiids have this same protection.

What is even more interesting, however, is that a considerable number of other butterflies that are perfectly edible have taken on the coloring and form of the heliconiids and ithomiids. Henry Walter Bates, in the course of his years of col-

A FORTIFIED NURSERY

Among certain Neotropical bell moths (above), the females have specialized scales on their abdomens. At egg-laying time these become detached and are deposited in a ring around the eggs like a miniature palisade (below), perhaps as a protection against wandering predatory insects. When the larvae hatch, they crawl over the needle-sharp stakes on a silken pathway which they spin themselves. A single palisade may contain as many as 3,000 stakes, which are glued so strongly to the leaf that they stand firm long after the larvae have departed.

PHYCIODES SPECIES

HELICONIUS SPECIES

HYPOTHYRIS AEMILIA

MELINAEA COMMA

MELINAEA MOTHONE

MECHANITIS MESSENOIDES

ONE OF THE CROWD

Despite the fact that the six orange-and-black butterflies shown here greatly resemble each other, they are not all related. The butterfly in the box at top is edible, but looks enough like all the inedible butterflies under it for predators to stay clear of it—a case of Batesian mimicry. The other five illustrate Müllerian mimicry, whereby different bad-tasting species have a specific warning pattern in common. Predators come to recognize the pattern through associative learning and ignore butterflies so marked.

lecting on the Amazon, was one of the first to notice this and thought that one species of butterfly mimicking another quite unrelated species might be the same sort of phenomenon as a butterfly mimicking a leaf or a patch of bark. He did not make much of it, however, until his return to England in 1859, when he read Darwin's great book *On the Origin of Species by Means of Natural Selection*. This furnished the explanation: an edible butterfly that happened to resemble an inedible or poisonous species would have a better chance of escaping predation—and the closer the resemblance, the more likely the survival. Mimicry, like protective coloration, has thus become a classic illustration of the power of natural selection.

There are cases of mimicry of one insect by another in all of the world's faunas, but the phenomenon is particularly striking in the tropics and reaches its greatest development in South America, where it was first observed and described. The heliconiids and ithomiids are the most common models among the butterflies, but wasps, as one might expect, have also acquired a whole host of mimics, especially among various families of moths and flies. The resemblances in appearance and behavior are sometimes so close that even the experienced naturalist is fooled. In fact, the only way to collect some kinds of wasp mimics is to catch all of the "wasps" in sight and look at them carefully before turning them loose again.

For mimicry, then, the model must be common, conspicuously marked and protected in some special way such as by a sting or by poisonous secretions. The mimic must be much rarer than the model and similar in both appearance and behavior. The theory, of course, is that the predator will first encounter the model and, learning that it is distasteful or dangerous, will also avoid the rarer mimic when it is encountered. The mimic is thus condemned to rarity, because if it were common, the advantage of conspicuous coloration would be lost both for mimic and for model.

This is the explanation worked out by Bates, and it is usually called "Batesian mimicry." Rather different is the phenomenon of "Müllerian mimicry," which was described later by the German zoologist Fritz Müller, also on the basis of observations made in Brazil. Müller noticed that bad-tasting butterflies of quite different groups sometimes resembled each other closely. There would be, he thought, an advantage in this: if the distasteful or dangerous insects all looked different, a bird or other predator would have to have tried to eat specimens of each kind to learn to avoid them. If, however, the different kinds of distasteful insects looked alike, as they do in Müllerian mimicry, fewer individual insects would be lost in the learning process.

THERE are, of course, also many cases of protective coloration among South American insects, especially among the inhabitants of the rain forest—cases in which insects copy leaves, twigs or bark with great exactness. Some of the best examples in South America are found among the beetles and the true bugs. There is, especially, one family of bugs, the Membracidae, or "treehoppers," that reaches its greatest development in the Neotropical region and is particularly interesting in this respect. These insects commonly live on twigs and stems, sucking out the juices of the plants which they pierce with their sharp beaks. They do not need to move much to get their food, and many species copy very exactly the spines or other protuberances of the stems on which they live. A great many of them, however, have gone far beyond the copying process and have developed extraordinary shapes with a variety of bizarre protuberances on their bodies.

They are small insects, hardly noticeable in nature, yet it is difficult to imagine any possible function for their weird forms. They remind one, in miniature, of some of the fantastic reptiles and mammals of the remote geological past: a case of nature having gone wild through sheer exuberance.

Related to the membracids are the fulgorids, or "lantern flies." These get their name from the largest species in the family, which has an enormously expanded peanut-shaped head. The lantern fly was first described in a book on the insects of Surinam, also known as Dutch Guiana, written by that extraordinary naturalist Madame Maria Sybilla Merian and published in 1705. Madame Merian described the inflated snout of this insect as luminous—hence the lantern. In most cases, Madame Merian's facts are accurate enough, but no one in modern times has seen anything luminescent about this insect, though the name "lantern" has persisted for it and its relatives. It has been suggested that perhaps Madame Merian happened upon a specimen which somehow had luminous bacteria in the snout.

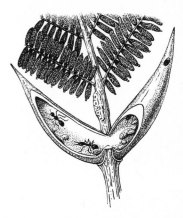

Soᴜᴛʜ America has its fair share of social insects—termites, ants, wasps and bees. None of the termites builds as large and spectacular a nest as some of the African and Australian species, but they are present everywhere in the warm tropics, carrying on their business of eating vegetation and, in particular, wood. The Neotropical Realm also has its fair share of ants—or perhaps more than its share. In the rain forest, one is always conscious of ants, sometimes acutely, since many of them have vicious stings, as painful as those inflicted by any of the fiercer wasps.

Ants, like most of the other inhabitants of the tropical forest, have developed many sorts of adaptations for life in the treetops. The number of kinds of trees that have developed special cavities that serve for ant nests is especially striking in the Neotropical region. Anyone working in the Amazonian forest soon learns especially to recognize two sorts of trees, *Triplaris* and *Cecropia*. Both have hollow stems which are used as nesting places by particular species of ants—and in both cases, the ants have especially vicious stings. One soon regrets any incautious disturbance of these trees. The advantages of these cooperative relationships to the ants are obvious: the trees provide not only nesting sites but also food in the form of special ant "nectaries" with sweet secretions. What the trees get out of the arrangement is less clear; a certain measure of protection is probably afforded by the presence of the stinging ants, and possibly there is nutrient value in the ant debris and droppings as well.

Ants have also found many ways of living in association with the epiphytic plants growing on trees high in the tropical forest. The orchids and bromeliads offer particularly favorable opportunities to ants for nest building, and the plants profit from the refuse of the ants. In the Amazonian forest several species of ants have gone even further, developing so-called "ant gardens" on the branches of trees. These appear to begin as ant nests, but when the ants bring food in the form of seeds of certain oil-bearing plants, some of the seeds inevitably germinate and the roots of the plants then help to bind the entire "garden" firmly together. Ants and plants then live in arboreal harmony, and while the whole arrangement is doubtless more accidental than "planned," it is just about as profitable to both as any carefully cultivated garden is to humans on the ground.

Perhaps the most striking of the Neotropical social insects are the stingless bees, or Meliponinae. These occur in the tropics of the Old World as well as

GIVE AND TAKE— ANTS IN AN ACACIA PLANT

There is more to the bull-horn acacias of Central and South America than meets the eye. As this cutaway drawing shows, their thorns often serve as a home for ants. When the horn-shaped thorns reach maturity, the ants gnaw holes in them, hollow out the insides and move in. There they live and tend their larvae, drawing for sustenance upon the honey-like secretion of nectar glands on the branches (below, left), and fruitlike bodies rich in oils, proteins and carbohydrates on the leaflets (below, right). In return for food and lodging, the ants, which are vicious stingers, keep the bull-horns free of nearly all insect pests.

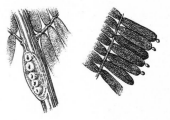

the New, but they are far more numerous in the American tropics than anywhere else. The two principal genera are *Melipona* and *Trigona:* the former relatively large, some almost as big as honeybees, and the latter smaller, some of them the smallest of all bees, only a twelfth of an inch in length.

The stingers of these creatures are vestigial—nonfunctional—but the bees can bite. They are especially apt to make for the hair of the head, and when dozens of them get entangled there, they can be extremely annoying. Some species seem to be attracted to sweat and are certainly to be counted among the nuisances of the forest.

The stingless bees are extraordinarily energetic nest builders. Henry Walter Bates described the activities of one Amazonian species thus: "The workers are generally seen collecting pollen in the same way as other bees, but great numbers are employed gathering clay. The rapidity and precision of their movements whilst thus engaged are wonderful. They first scrape the clay with their jaws; the small portions gathered are then cleared by the anterior paws and passed to the second pair of feet, which, in their turn, convey them to the large foliated expansions of the hind shanks which are adapted normally in bees, as everyone knows, for the collection of pollen. The middle feet pat the growing pellets of mortar on the hind legs to keep them in a compact shape as the particles are successively added. The little hodsmen soon have as much as they can carry, and they then fly off. . . . They construct their combs in any suitable crevice in trunks of trees or perpendicular banks, and the clay is required to build up a wall so as to close the gap, with the exception of a small orifice for their own entrance and exit."

Some species of these bees collect the sticky sap of various plants, presumably for use in construction. One *Trigona* has become a minor pest to banana growers in this way, nicking the ridges of the green fruit to collect the milky juice that exudes. This does not harm the fruit except that it leaves a row of small black spots when the bananas become ripe—and American buyers do not like to have spots on their bananas.

Stingless or not, these bees make honey, and at least one species, *Melipona beecheii*, was extensively domesticated by Aztecs and Mayas in pre-Columbian times. In fact, this was their main source of honey, since the true honeybee is an Old World insect which was first brought to America by Europeans. This same species is still cultivated by the Indians of Yucatán, who use hollowed-out logs as hives.

THE most successful of all insects are the beetles, members of the order Coleoptera—there are at least 300,000 species of them in the world. South America has its due proportion of the world's species, but it seems that they have to be searched for more diligently than elsewhere. Henry Walter Bates thought that beetles were less obvious in the Amazon forest than in England—even though they were infinitely more numerous. This again was because most beetles secrete themselves in hidden corners and shady places. They also tend to be inconspicuous because of their protective coloration—though some of them are brilliant enough to be used as jewelry.

The giants among the South American Coleoptera are the rhinoceros beetles. Though not as large as the goliath beetles of the Old World tropics, they are formidable-looking creatures. The males have great horns which are their primary weapons in fighting each other: they use them as wrestlers use their arms, striving to raise an opponent bodily and send him crashing to the ground.

Sometimes, after the heat of battle, a victorious male may rush a female, and probably mistaking her for still another enemy, lift her up and carry her away— which has given rise to a romantic, if mistaken, notion that the males court their mates in cave-man fashion.

Among the South American beetles are the brightest of all fireflies. The familiar fireflies of the northern continent belong to the beetle family Lampyridae, and they have their Neotropical forms, too, which put on spectacular evening displays in the grassy, open savannas. But the most brilliant species belong to quite a different family, the click beetles, or Elateridae. The luminescent forms, which are found only in the New World tropics, belong to the genus *Pyrophorus*, which has more than 100 species. All have two light-producing spots on either side of the thorax, which glow at night like twin headlights. In his book *A Naturalist in Brazil*, Konrad Guenther vividly described the appearance of these extraordinary creatures:

I WAS once sitting on the verandah of a lonely house in the forest of northern Pernambuco, when such a beetle came flying up; it had two greenish-blue lanterns on its shoulders, so that it seemed, like a locomotive, to be lighting its own track. It was a magnificent sight: especially when more of these living aerial locomotives came floating up and flying across the verandah. I have caught such luminous beetles, some species of which have a third light on the underside of their body; even by daylight the luminous organs were perceptible as yellow spots on the hinder edge of the brown scutum or neck-shield, and they blazed up at once if I carried the long, narrow beetle into the dark. I always kept such a 'cucujo,' as the insect is called in the West Indies, in a glass on my bed-table, so that I might be able to tell the time in the night. It filled the whole room with a faint green light, which was intensified if I shook the glass."

The luminosity of these beetles is truly astounding, and furthermore not only the male and female but even the eggs and larva shine at night. One of the largest of all, a grublike creature two inches long, has females which emit a colored light: "The first segment of the body," Guenther wrote, "glowed like a red-hot ball of iron; the rest of the body followed like a broad blue, or sometimes yellow, streak of fire, and the constrictions of the segments gave it the appearance of a string of gems."

Besides insects, there are of course a great variety of spiders, scorpions, centipedes, millepedes and ticks in the Neotropical region. Ticks, in the dry season, can be among the major pests. Little balls made up of hundreds of "seed ticks" wait on the tip of a branch for some animal or man to brush past, and one can spend hours picking them off one by one from the body. Experienced naturalists used to have a ball of beeswax which was rolled on the body, embedding the ticks and saving the trouble of picking off and killing them individually. Nowadays much of this can be avoided by the judicious use of insect repellents applied to exposed parts of the body and to clothing.

There are splendid centipedes and scorpions in South America, but I suspect other parts of the tropics have larger and more venomous ones. South America does have the largest spider in the world, the hairy tarantula, which may be as big as 10 inches across with its eight legs extended. Tarantulas bite if provoked, but their poison is overrated. I have never heard of danger to man from these huge beasts, but at the same time I have never been tempted to try picking one up barehanded; though their behavior is docile, they do look frightening. They have sometimes been called "bird spiders" because they are reputed to kill birds. This is not a common occurrence, but Madame Merian in her book published in 1705 drew a picture of a spider trapping a hummingbird, and Henry Walter Bates described a similar occurrence to which he was an actual witness in a forest on the upper Amazon. "It [the spider] was close beneath a deep crevice in the tree, across which was stretched a dense white web," he wrote. "The lower part of the web was broken, and two small birds, finches, were entangled in the pieces; they were about the size of the English siskin, and I judged the two to be male and female. One of them was quite dead, the other lay under the body of the spider not quite dead, and was smeared with the filthy liquor or saliva exuded by the monster. I drove away the spider and took the birds, but the second one soon died." Bates said this particular spider had a body two inches long, but that the legs expanded seven inches and the entire body and legs were covered with coarse gray and reddish hairs.

Spiders, ticks, scorpions, insects, along with crabs, shrimps, lobsters and such marine and fresh-water animals, go to make up the phylum Arthropoda —the animals with jointed appendages. An interesting relative of these creatures—perhaps similar to the first arthropod way back in the dim geological past—is a caterpillarlike animal called peripatus. There are many species of these in the wet forests of the various continents, but the first was described from the West Indies, and they are found all through the American tropics as well as in Africa and other parts of the world.

THE peripatus was actually at first thought to be a type of slug, because its discoverer, the Reverend Landsdowne Guilding, a 19th Century naturalist, failed to recognize the stubby appendages along its sides as legs. He gave it the name of *Limax juliformis* in 1825, and it was not until many years later that the ancient little animal was examined in more detail. Then it was found that it did really have legs, and that these legs were each equipped with a pair of claws, and that it walked on these legs very nicely. It was also found that twin appendages on its head were not, as the Reverend Guilding had thought, the kind of tentacles a slug might have, but sensitive antennae. All of this made the creature even more confusing: though it had some insect characteristics, it was not an insect; and while it was tempting to consider it a worm, it obviously was not a worm. It was classified at last as a "walking worm," and so named— and today we know some 80 species of peripatus in a dozen genera and two families; and we know also that it is an animal which has been walking this earth for some 500 million years, perhaps one of the very first to emerge from the sea to start life on the land.

South America and its northern isthmus form, above all, a realm of many habitats, and insects abound in all of them. Each of the great biomes has its specialties—the pampas, the savanna, the rain forest, the cloud forest—but perhaps the most striking example of the extremes in living habits to which insects will go is found in the high Andes. Here, at altitudes above 15,000 feet, with scarcely any vegetation, live a surprising number of small butterflies. There are blue ones, yellow ones and white ones, and all of them are constantly struggling against some of the fiercest winds that blow. And even higher, at the extreme limit of vegetation, lives the hardiest of all. One of the most specialized of all butterflies, it is white with mother-of-pearl spots, and its life appears to revolve around a single plant, *Perezia atacamensis*, a large-flowered annual which still manages to grow at these heights—two tenacious species which survive at the very edge of our planet, where earth meets sky.

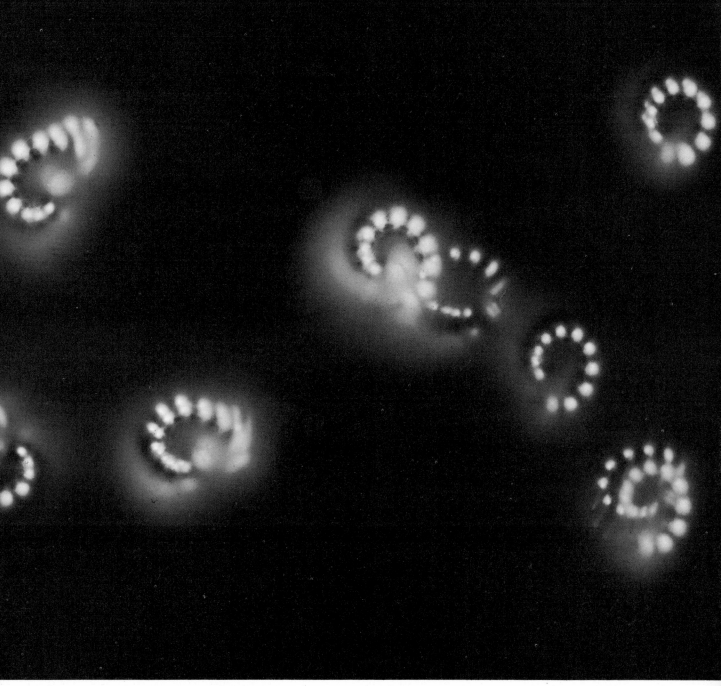

RAILROAD WORMS—GRUBS OF A SOUTH AMERICAN BEETLE—LIGHT UP LIKE TRAINS WHEN DISTURBED AND GLOW FOR SEVERAL MINUTES

An Insect Eden

An enormous evolutionary workshop that seems never to shut down, the seasonless rain forests have helped give the Neotropical region one of the world's most distinctive insect faunas. Here live crawling and flying things that look more like plants than animals, others that are mirror copies of unrelated species, and still others that have colors more brilliant—and startling—even than flowers.

A STICKY EXCRETION, FIRED FROM GLANDS AT EITHER SIDE OF ITS MOUTH, PROTECTS THE PERIPATUS BY MIRING DOWN INSECT ATTACKERS

A Walking Worm

The many-legged creature shown here is a peripatus, one of the infrequently seen and little-studied inhabitants of forests in several parts of the world. This Neotropical species, generally from two to three inches long, lives under logs or rotting vegetation and comes out at night or during rain, apparently to feed on insects and worms. It is velvety to the touch and has a three-segmented head and some two dozen pairs of stumpy legs, on each of which there are curved claws.

Evolutionally ancient, the peripatus seems to be descended from a connecting link between the annelids, which include the earthworms and leeches, and the arthropods, which include the crustaceans and insects. It has features similar to those of both groups—the musculature and cuticle-covered skin of the annelids, the bladelike jaws and ability to molt of the arthropods. It breathes like an arthropod though air tubes piercing its body, but lacks the arthropod's closing mechanisms and so loses much moisture. To guard against desiccation, it crawls about only when the humidity is above 90 per cent.

BIRTH OF A PERIPATUS, an event rarely observed, here takes place in a laboratory. The first of two emerges *(above)*, and while it crawls over the mother's back *(below)*, the second pokes out an antenna. Each birth took about an hour, terminating a process that began when sperm deposited on the female's body created an ulcer through which male cells entered.

THE BROKEN LINES AND DRAB COLOR OF A SOUTH AMERICAN MANTID CAMOUFLAGE IT, CONCEALING IT FROM PREDATORS AND PREY ALIKE

A Riotous Diversity

Probably nowhere else on earth are insects more diversified or more specialized than in the tropical forests of South and Central America. The reasons for this are many. The rich flora, in providing an almost limitless number of niches for small animals to occupy, has enabled the insects to radiate in many directions. Moreover, the abundance of insect eaters in the forests, especially birds, has imposed upon the insects the strictest kind of natural selection and caused many to develop extreme—often bizarre—defenses. In addition, the relative ecological and climatic stability, particularly of the rain forests, for some 13 million years past has permitted many complex insects to survive there—species that might possibly have died out in a more varying environment.

A GLASSY-WINGED TREEHOPPER has a hump on its back terminating in a rod-shaped structure without any known function. Entomologists consider this a case of evolution run wild.

162

THE LONG TONGUE OF A SOUTH AMERICAN BEE ENABLES IT TO LAP FOOD FROM LEAVES AND TO SUCK NECTAR FROM THE HEARTS OF FLOWERS

A SEED-SHAPED COCKROACH shows the flat shape that allows it to hide in cracks and crevices. In contrast to the northern species, the tropical varieties are often quite brightly colored.

FLAT ON A LEAF, a butterfly is camouflaged by the partial transparency of its wings. This species normally flies with two other species that look like it; all are unpleasant to the taste.

163

A NEW YORK KATYDID appears less specialized than the Neotropical species opposite, which have evolved at a faster rate. The climate permits them to have several generations a year.

GENUS TYPOPHYLLUM

DYSONIA PUNCTIFRONS

AGANACRIS INSECTIVORA

How Not to Be Eaten

In the tropical forests, as elsewhere, the insects that look least edible are the ones least likely to be eaten. Thus many have evolved to look like leaves, plants and other insects more aggressive or less palatable than themselves, vivid evidence of the power of natural selection. Shown opposite are the results of this culling among the Neotropical katydids. The three in the top row opposite all look like leaves, even to the veins and plantlike blemishes that leaves have. Some insects of this type complete the illusion by remaining motionless during the day. Others sway back and forth gently as though a wind were rustling them.

In the middle row the katydid at left and the nymph in the center resemble lichens, with their white and gray and black patterns. The unidentified one at the right, also in a nymphal stage, has long green legs and antennae that tend to resemble the veins in leaves. The red-winged katydid at bottom left mimics a stinging vespoid wasp, and the one next to it a dried twig. Some katydids do not mimic anything specific at all. The lacy one at bottom right relies on a disruptive pattern to break up its form, making it difficult to pick out in the forest.

AEGIMIA ELONGATA

AUGARA MIRABILIS

GENUS LICHENOCHRUS

GENUS UNIDENTIFIED

GENUS PARAPHIDNIA

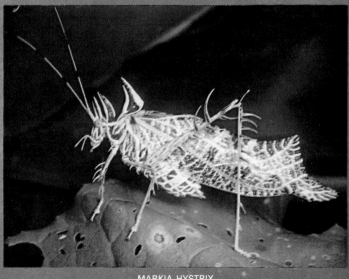

MARKIA HYSTRIX

Torrents of Butterflies

Outstanding among the insects of the world are the butterflies and the moths of the Neotropical region. So wide is the representation of many of the large groups which occur only here that thousands of species still remain unstudied, while perhaps thousands more await discovery in the lofty canopies of the rain forests. Occasionally, the vastness of these populations is dramatized when certain butterflies are moved into mass migrations by unknown inner or outer forces. One such swarm, made up of members

LOOKING LIKE UPRIGHT LEAVES, BRIGHTLY COLORED PHOEBIS BUTTERFLIES CLUSTER ON A SAND BAR TO DRINK. THE BUTTERFLIES OF THE NEOTRO

of all the known species in one particular part of Argentina, had a leading edge a mile and a half wide and took 11 minutes to pass overhead. The genus *Phoebis*, to which the butterflies below belong, has many strong fliers and is famous for its migrations.

Phoebis butterflies have been seen flapping across the ocean toward certain death, and one flight was observed for a week on a seemingly quite pointless migration—it flew down a river mornings, turned around at midday and flew upstream afternoons.

ON ARE UNEXCELLED FOR THEIR BRILLIANCE, AND MANY HAVE WING PATTERNS ASTOUNDING IN THE RICHNESS AND THE VARIETY OF THEIR DESIGN

1. NECYRIA ZANETA

2. LYROPTERYX APOLLONIA

3. MESOSEMIA ASA

4. CREMNA ACTORIS HETEROEA

5. STALACHTIS PHAEDUSA

6. LYMNAS PIXE

7. NYMPHIDIUM MANTUS

8. MESENE MARGARETTA

9. CARTEA VITULA UCAYALA

THE ENORMOUS VARIETY to be found within just one group of butterflies in the Neotropical region is shown here by only 16 members of the metalmark family, which totals perhaps 2,000 species. The multiplicity of colors, patterns and wing shapes of the metalmarks is staggering and confounds even collectors, who are often hard put to identify individual specimens. Yet behind every color pattern, every variation in wing shape, seems to lie some evolutionary imperative which, if found, explains the appearance of the butterfly concerned.

Thus many species, no matter how conspicuous they may seem in a photograph like the one above, may be cryptic in the wild, their colors and patterns helping to conceal them in their

10. EUSELASIA ERYTHRAEA

11. LEUCOCHIMONA LAGORA

12. SEMOMESIA CAPANEA

13. MESOSEMIA ZONALIS

14. RHETUS DYSONII PSECAS

16. HELICOPIS ACIS

15. ANCYLURIS AULESTES MICANS

own habitats. Still others may stand out there, either boldly warning predators that they taste bad or, as in the case of mimics, resembling butterflies that actually do so closely that predators will pass them by. In others, the vividly contrasting bands and patches on their wings break up their outlines as they flit about, making them elusive targets. Some have prom-inent eyespots on their wings and flash these to startle and con-fuse predators. The tails of the *Helicopis* (*bottom right, above*), on the other hand, may draw attack to these expendable parts. And still other species may depend upon a distinctive appearance to make them immediately recognizable to mem-bers of their own species—and especially to the opposite sex.

GAUDILY COLORED, *Pseudatteria leopardina* is the brightest member of a moth genus found only in South America. It has been little studied: experts have not yet even established whether it is a twilight- or day-flying species. The males and females are almost impossible to tell apart, but mysteriously males remain rare—invariably it is the female that is caught.

DELICATELY TRANSPARENT, *Chorinea faunus* is shown against a checkered paper to demonstrate how its film-thin wing membranes lack the coating of colorful scales which most other butterflies have. Outlined in black, *Chorinea faunus*, yet another of the metalmarks, has color in only one area—its long tails. These are often a brilliant blue, set off by red patches.

A STORM OF MOTHS swirls around entomologist Henry Fleming at Portachuelo Pass in Venezuela. Drawn by the light of 100-watt bulbs, migrating moths representing hundreds of species swarmed in such numbers night after night that Fleming and his associates were able in one season to cull more than 70,000 specimens to ship to the United States for study.

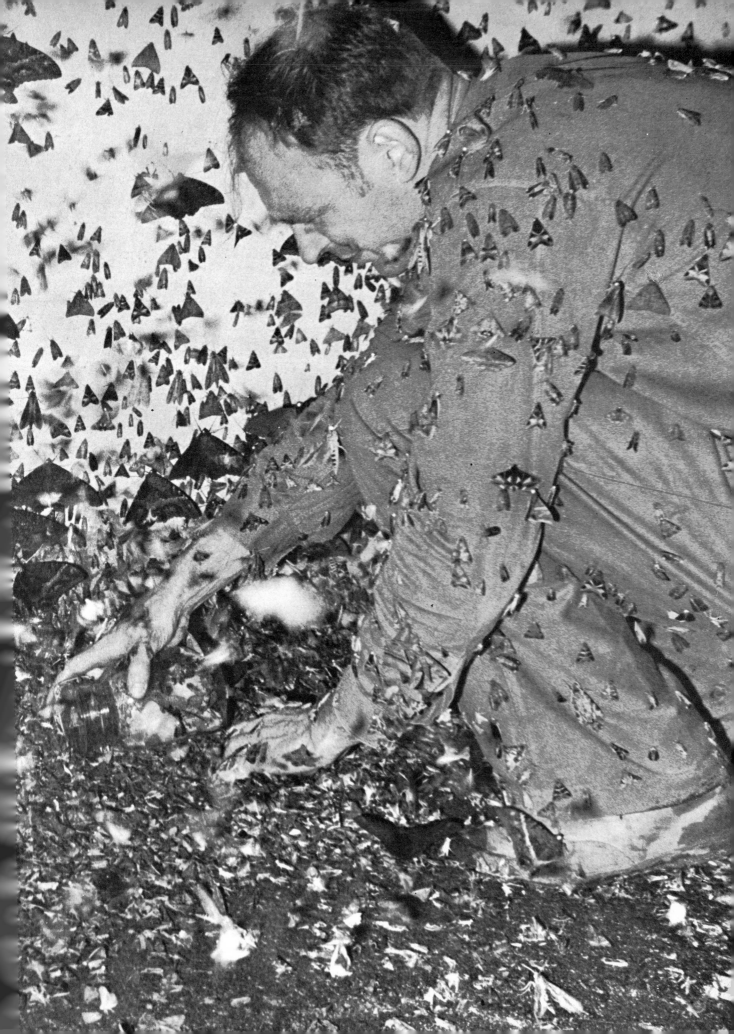

A ROTTING CACAO POD full of rain water attracts two female mosquitoes of the genus *Trichoprosopon*. In the enlargement at right, they are shown laying their eggs on the water.

A Curtain of Mosquitoes

Because conditions in the tropics are ideally suited to their development, mosquitoes have proliferated here as nowhere else. In the rain forests, for example, temperatures hover in the 80s, the air is saturated with humidity, and the light is crepuscular even at high noon. Few mosquitoes are found flying in open country when the sun is shining. With their habitat so accommodating, it is not surprising that they have come to exploit all of its niches and that in the forests hangs a veritable curtain of mosquitoes. One group dwells close to the forest floor, another group lives a little higher up, another higher still, and so on, until the upper limits of the forest canopy are reached.

Every species has a certain time of day at which it feeds, and this is also when it mates or lays its eggs. All deposit their eggs on the surface of water, but some prefer one site over another—*Trichoprosopon* (*above*), for example, will lay only in such ready-made containers as coconut husks and rot holes.

TWISTING AND TURNING ON ITSELF, FORMING OXBOWS, CURVES, FULL CIRCLES AND CUTOFFS, THE KULUENE RIVER OF BRAZIL'S MATO GROSSO

8 The Rivers and Their Denizens

ASSIC EXAMPLE OF AN AMAZON BASIN RIVER. THE KULUENE FLOWS INTO THE XINGU, WHICH JOINS THE MAMMOTH AMAZON NEAR ITS MOUTH

THREE great river systems dominate most of the area of the South American continent, determining vast reaches of its flora and fauna. In the north is the Orinoco, which flows north and then east into the Atlantic near Trinidad. Farther south, almost bisecting the great bulge that comprises the upper half of the continent, is the Amazon, mightiest of rivers. Still farther south, and almost connecting with a branch of the Madeira, one of the Amazon's tributaries, is the Paraná-Paraguay river system, which, flowing generally southward, drains into the Atlantic at Buenos Aires.

The Amazon and Orinoco rivers actually do connect through tributary streams, and between them they form the greatest river system on earth. The Nile and the Missouri-Mississippi may be a little longer, but neither carries a fourth as much water or drains anywhere near as large an area. More than a third of the entire continent—some two and a half million square miles—is dominated by the Amazon and Orinoco. Only recently it was calculated that the Amazon's average flow is 7.5 million cubic feet per second—twice what it was hitherto thought to be—or enough to flood the entire state of New York to a depth of six inches in a single day. Near its mouth, this tremendous river reaches widths up to 200 miles; for most of its 3,300-mile length it is more than five miles wide, and the muddy fresh water it discharges into the Atlantic Ocean is still detectable 200 miles from shore. Many of the tributaries of the Amazon are themselves great rivers—the Rio Negro, Japura, Napo, Tapajos, to name a few of them, some running more than 1,000 miles into the interior.

THE Amazon River system is connected with the Orinoco by means of a waterway called the Casiquiare Canal, a unique phenomenon possible only in a flooded land. The Casiquiare was reportedly first navigated in 1561 by a Spaniard named Lope de Aguirre, in the course of his search for the fabled golden city of El Dorado. Its existence as an actual connection was first reported by a priest, Father Cristóbal de Acuña, in 1639. The 125-mile length of this unusual stream is rarely traversed even now, both because of its inaccessibility and because life there is made miserable by hordes of biting insects. The water flows from the Orinoco to the Rio Negro, dropping about 70 feet. Thus the two great connected river systems form what is virtually a vast inland sea through whose numberless streams a fresh-water fish can swim for thousands of miles.

One of the things noticed by travelers in the interior of South America is that while most lowland rivers or their tributaries are muddy, some are clear, although of a brownish color. The Rio Negro, which meets the Amazon at the inland city of Manaus, is the largest of these clear, "black-water" streams, and at its mouth, in flood season, its dark waters push aside the muddy waters of the main Amazon for several miles downstream. The black-water rivers and creeks invariably drain heavy-rain forest areas and usually flow over crystalline rocks rather than sedimentary ones. Their color is believed to come from the leaching of dead vegetation; the water itself is almost as "soft" as distilled water and rather highly acid. While some fishes of muddy streams do not appear to be greatly affected by black water, others do not enter such rivers. Hence the fishes of the black streams are often a quite different lot from those of muddy ones.

South America is the richest of all continents in the number of species of fresh-water fishes. Though the fish fauna has still not been well studied, and no one can make an exact count, fish experts estimate that there are at least 2,500 species, of which perhaps 2,000 occur in the great connected river basins from the Orinoco in Venezuela to the Plata system in Argentina. The greatest variety exists in the Amazon itself. It has recently been estimated that upward of 700 different kinds of fishes are to be found at one or another time of the year within a 20-mile radius of Manaus—almost as many as are found in all the fresh waters of the entire continent of North America. West of the Andes, however, the story is quite different. There are only about 30 different kinds of fishes in the short, steep streams that rush down the mountains of Chile into the Pacific. And in all the west-flowing rivers of Peru, Ecuador and Colombia combined, the total is believed to be under 125.

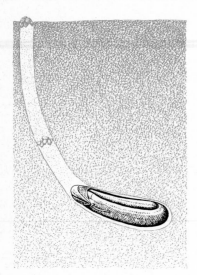

A FISH WITHOUT WATER

The South American lungfish shown here is about to pass the dry season underground in a state of torpor. A swamp dweller, it retreats into the mud as soon as there is no longer water to keep it comfortably wet. At first it pushes up through the soft, soupy mud for gulps of air. But as the mud hardens, it stoppers its burrow with loosely fitting mud plugs, curls its tail in front of its head, and secretes a moisture-conserving film around its body. Not until the arrival of the rainy season does it stir again. Awakened by water filling its burrow, it pushes out the plugs and wriggles its way up to the swamp.

This South American fish fauna is very ancient, the majority of it belonging to groups that were already established in the days when the dinosaurs were disappearing or dead. What is more, there seem to have been no significant fish invasions since that time. The result of the 60 million years or more of isolation is no less than 17 families that are unique to South and Central America, and with an over-all richness and peculiarity of types that make tropical American fishes one of the world's faunal marvels.

Aside from their distinctiveness, the most remarkable thing about South American fishes is that they ever got there at all. Australia, also an isolated continent, has fresh-water fishes whose ancestors for the most part might well have arrived from the sea and adapted to fresh water later on, but this is not true of South America. On the record of the fossil evidence and certain evolutionary characteristics too complicated to go into here, it is fairly clear that the fishes of South America, like other animals, came across some sort of land bridge, in their case via a chain of fresh-water rivers, lakes and ponds. The odd thing is that some of their closest relatives are found in Africa, an ocean away! The only way to explain this is to theorize that there were once common ancestors which existed in a tropical area in the great, ancient northern world continent, and that these either worked their way down into Africa and across a no-longer-existing land bridge into South America, or went, pond by pond, stream by stream, out of Eurasia, into North America and from there into South America. Either way, it is a long trip, one that is almost incomprehensible to us in the world of today.

The vast majority of South American river fishes belong to three large groups: the catfishes, characins and cichlids. In addition to these, the continent has some very peculiar smaller groups. Strangest of all is the family which includes the electric eels, numbering some 40 species. Although they are not true eels, all are elongate, eel-like creatures with no fin on the back and one very long fin below. They can swim forward or backward with almost equal facility. The ancient lungfish group is represented by one species, a creature reaching two feet in length, which lives in swampy areas and greatly resembles the lungfishes of Africa. A strange little creature known as the leaf fish gets its name because, floating in mid-water, it looks exactly like a dead leaf—two species of it are known here. Finally, there are also in South America two species of a remarkable, ancient family, the osteoglossids.

MUCH more numerous than these oddities, and swarming throughout the continent from Panama to Ecuador and Argentina, are a host of little cyprinodonts, many of which give birth to living young. These are commonly called top minnows and are much more important than their tiny size would indicate. Not only are many of them prized throughout the world as home aquarium fishes, but most of them, including the well-loved guppy, are predators of the aquatic larvae of mosquitoes and thus important in the fight against malaria.

The rest of the fishes of the South American rivers are nearly all members of salt-water groups which, for one reason or another, are able to invade fresh water. Among them are tarpons, a few shad- or herring-like fishes, some anchovies, some drumfishes, a few sharks, sawfishes and a number of species of dangerous stingrays.

Perhaps the most famous river fish of South America is one of the two osteoglossids—the giant redfish, or pirarucú, of the Amazon, called paiche in Peru and arapaima in British Guiana. It is often regarded as the biggest of all fresh-

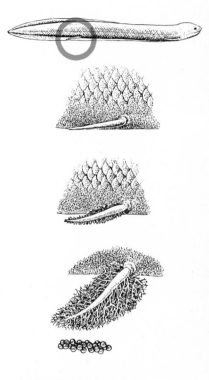

A MYSTERIOUS FRINGE

One of the unexplained mysteries of the South American lungfish is the appearance of many-branched filaments on the hind fins of the male (circle) during the breeding season. These take about three weeks to develop, turning bright red in the process and ultimately becoming two or three inches long, as shown in the last of the three enlargements. It has not been determined whether they are accessory breathing organs or whether they are used as a way of bringing oxygen to the eggs during brooding, at which time they are inserted directly among the eggs.

water fishes, reportedly reaching a length of nine or 10 feet and a weight of 300 pounds, though these figures certainly represent extremes. In any case, its claim, like that of the various kinds of giant catfishes, can be honored only by ignoring the giant sturgeon of northern waters and the giant sawfishes of the tropics, on the grounds that neither spend their entire lives in fresh water.

The pirarucú, heavily fished for 300 years, is the most important animal food of the Amazonian region—some millions of pounds of its flesh are dried every year. The fish are speared or shot with arrows, and the meat is cut into longitudinal strips for drying. The dried strips are then rolled up into bundles which are a standard article of trade on the river. Opinions about its taste vary, though few foreigners have shown any enthusiasm about the dried product. Its great virtue, like that of dried cod, is convenience rather than flavor.

The smaller osteoglossid cousin of the pirarucú, the aruaná, rarely grows to more than 30 inches. It broods its eggs in its mouth and is one of the most graceful of all swimmers. All of the osteoglossids possess very large scales and a bony tongue—the tongue bone of the pirarucú, covered thickly with small, pointed teeth, is used as a grater in Amazonian kitchens.

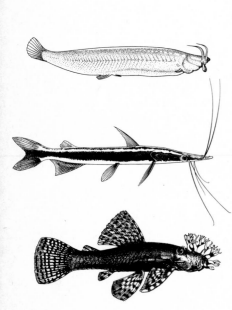

A STRANGE TRIO
OF CATFISHES

The catfishes that inhabit the rivers of South America sometimes vary so greatly in appearance that it is difficult to believe that they all belong to the same group. The fish at top, barely an inch long, burrows in the sand and has no eyes whatsoever. It has been seen in only a few rock pools near a remote waterfall on the Rio Negro. The more common shovel-nosed catfish (middle), about a foot long, is notable for its long, forward-probing barbels. The barbels on the five-inch armored catfish (bottom) grow in bushy clusters on the males only.

THE South American catfishes are classified into 12 different families, each with numerous species, and make up about half of the total fish fauna. They show an immense variety in size and form. The biggest, called lau-lau in British Guiana and piraibá on the Amazon, is very probably the world's largest catfish. Reliable authorities cite record specimens nearly 10 feet long and close to five feet in girth, which would, at a guess, weigh between 400 and 500 pounds. What is more, the average size of specimens caught is very large, whereas the reputedly larger pirarucú averages only 50 to 60 pounds in the fishes brought to market. Thus, the argument over the world's largest fresh-water fish goes on.

These big catfishes have a number of smaller catfish cousins in South American waters that run up to four or five feet in length. There are also hundreds of still smaller species from an inch to a foot long. The suckermouth armored catfishes constitute the largest single family of South American catfishes. These creatures do not have the usual smooth catfish skin, but are covered with a close-fitting armor of bony plates which in turn are closely set with spiny tubercles similar to the denticles of a shark's skin. All of the 415 species either scrape algae from submerged trees or stones with their powerful sucking mouths or scratch around on the bottom for detritus. Certain forms are widely used for food—cooked "in the shell" in their own armor.

One of the catfish families, the Pygidiidae, has gone in for reduction in size and for quasi-parasitic habits. Some of its species are the smallest of all South American fishes—about an inch long and as thick as a toothpick. They feed in the gills of larger fishes, sucking blood from the gill filaments. The most notorious members of the family are several species of the candirú, sometimes called "the only vertebrate parasite of man," though this is stretching the definition of parasite, since the association with man is accidental. These tiny bloodsucking fishes occasionally wriggle into the urethral openings of men or women bathing in the streams; the erectile, backward-pointing spines on the head make it impossible to remove the fish without cutting, and they cause an excruciating pain.

The fishes most often seen in South American rivers are the characins, which outnumber all others. They swarm in all the waters from Buenos Aires to Panama. Their size range is extreme—one of the world's greatest and most widely known game fishes, the dorado of the Paraná and Paraguay rivers, is a characin, the largest one in South America. These great, golden fish resemble large salmon in shape, and like salmon they leap waterfalls during their upstream breeding migrations. Adults weigh from 40 to 60 pounds, and they fight as well as or better than salmon when hooked, as the members of the renowned Dorado Club in Buenos Aires will testify.

Another well-known group of characins is the large, deep-bodied species called pacus by the Indians, who prize them as food. The pacus are an oddity among fishes because they eat fruit that falls from trees along the riverbanks.

Finally, the characin family also includes that most dangerous of all South American fishes, the dread piranha. Closely related to the fruit-eating pacus and similar to them in appearance, the various forms of piranha—there are more than a score of species—range from the size of a man's hand to nearly two feet in length. Four are known to be dangerous to man: far from being vegetarians, they are fierce, carnivorous animals. George Myers, a distinguished ichthyologist of Stanford University, not given to exaggeration, describes the fiercest of the piranha types as follows:

"A fish only a foot long with teeth so sharp and jaws so strong that it can chop out a piece of flesh from a man or an alligator as neatly as a razor, or clip off a finger or a toe, bone and all, with the dispatch of a meat-cleaver! A fish afraid of nothing, which attacks any animal, whatever its size, like lightning! A fish which never attacks singly but always in schools of a hundred or a thousand! A fish which is actually attracted by splashing and commotion in water! And a fish which, when it smells blood, turns into a raging demon! This is the piranha, feared as no other animal is feared throughout the whole length of South America."

The last of the three big fish groups is the basslike cichlid family, the best known of which are the two common Amazon and Guiana species of tucunare— or luckananee, as they are called in Guiana. The smaller of these two species, *Cichla ocellaris*, grows to two feet; the larger, *Cichla temensis*, almost a foot longer. They are not only hard fighters equal in game qualities to North American black bass but they are among the most prized food fishes in South American rivers. Many other smaller species of cichlids are found throughout the continent north of Buenos Aires and east of the Chilean and Peruvian Andes; these resemble in appearance and behavior the North American sunfishes.

I F we played the game of which fishes are the mostest, South America's would win on several counts: the pirarucú and the giant catfish as the biggest of strictly fresh-water fishes; the candirú as the most insidious; the piranha as the fiercest; and to this we could add the electric eel, perhaps calling it the most extraordinary. A large electric eel, five or six feet in length, can produce outputs as high as 650 volts, and a three-foot eel can regularly produce 350 volts. There are no clearly documented cases of people being killed by shocks from these eels, but it is entirely possible. In two instances known to me, men from geological crews exploring in the upper Orinoco country for oil were found drowned in rather small ponds, though the men were known to be good swimmers. The only likely explanation seemed to be that they had been knocked unconscious by a shock from an eel.

The South American electric eel is one of a select family of fishes which all share the interesting internal arrangement whereby an important part of their muscle tissue has been modified to produce significant amounts of electricity. All animals which have a nervous system produce a minute amount of electricity,

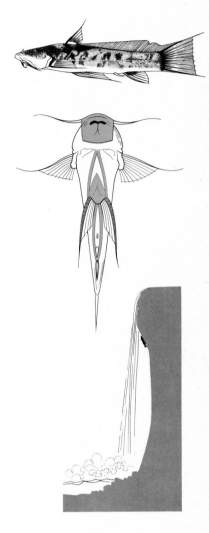

A VERSATILE CLIMBER

Although a clumsy and awkward swimmer, this rather ordinary-looking Colombian catfish can climb the stone face of a waterfall. A look at its underside shows why. The fish has a sucker mouth that enables it to fasten itself to objects and stay put, even in raging torrents. In addition, there is a bony plate on the fish's belly, controlled by powerful muscles. Moved forward, the plate brings with it the attached ventral fins. Tiny, sharp, backward-pointing teeth on the fins grab hold of surfaces and prevent backsliding. By alternate action of mouth and plate, the fish can hitch its way up a 20-foot wall in about half an hour.

but in the vast majority the current is extremely small and confined entirely within the body—e.g., it takes an electrocardiograph to register the current produced in the human heart. What makes the electric fishes extraordinary is that they can release electricity outside their bodies, and that the amounts released are appreciable, ranging from mild tingles to paralyzing and fatal shocks.

The electric eel is by far the most potent of these electric fishes. Four fifths of its elongated body is made up of the electricity-producing tissue; all of its vital organs are crowded into the head end. This makes it really a very short fish with a very long tail, and the functions of its highly charged tail are to provide it with protection, food and the ability to detect objects in the muddy waters where it lives, all through electricity.

THERE are three electricity-producing organs in the tail of the electric eel, each of which seems to have a separate though related function. The largest of the three—the main battery, so to speak—produces the high-voltage discharges. It starts at the head end of the tail and runs for about two thirds of its length, tapering at the hind end. It is a paired organ—i.e., there is one such organ on either side of the tail. The electric cells within the organs are arranged in series, like storage batteries in the old-type, electricity-driven submarines. Just what these cells consist of has not yet been fully ascertained, but it is thought that they are muscles in which the contractile tissue has disappeared, so that all that is left is a concentration of the motor end plates, the electricity-producing nerve terminals which in any muscle govern muscular action.

Where the large electric organ tapers toward the hind end of the tail, another, smaller paired organ begins. This one is known as the bundles of Sachs, and it releases discharges about one tenth as strong as those of the large organ. But whereas the major discharges are released in trains of 10 or so at a time (and up to 300 or 400 per second in a vigorous eel), the bundles of Sachs send out single impulses at the rate of 20 or 30 per second. These discharges seem to function as a sort of locating device, replacing the eyes, which, as a young eel matures, become clouded and useless, possibly as a result of being damaged by repeated electric shocks.

A third electric organ, called the organs of Hunter, lies along the base of the anal fin. Long and slender, it runs the full length of the tail. Its discharges are very faint and, though they seem to be related to the major discharges, their function is unknown.

Another oddity of the electric eel is that it breathes air—it must rise to the surface every 15 minutes or so, or it will drown. It has neither lungs nor gills, but numerous small folds in the mouth, covering tongue and palate, that are

AN AQUATIC ELECTROCUTIONER

Nervous electricity, a characteristic of all higher animals, has been adapted by the electric eel into a powerful weapon. An inch-long baby eel can make a man's hand tingle; a yard-long mature eel can stun a horse. Most of an eel's body is devoted to its batteries—the bundles of Sachs (A), the large electric organ (B), and the little-understood organs of Hunter (C). The bundles of Sachs generate a weak electric field with the eel's head end as the positive pole and its tail end as the negative. A fish that swims too near distorts this field (middle drawing). The eel responds by triggering its main powerhouse (far right). This potent mass of electric cells emits short blasts of direct current that can exceed 350 volts, stunning or killing a hapless victim.

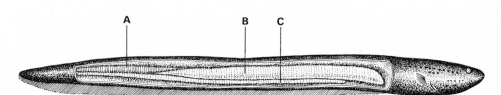

specialized for absorbing oxygen. In the laboratory, electric eels can be kept out of water for hours at a time; all that is necessary to keep them alive is to moisten the mouth once in a while with water.

Fishes with lungs do exist in South America, however. The most famous is *Lepidosiren paradoxa*, the Neotropical representative of the lungfishes. This single species of South American lungfish is found through much of the Paraná and Amazon river systems, but it is most characteristic of the great swamps of the Chaco. These warm, muddy waters have a low oxygen content, so that the relatively few fishes living there require some special adaptation for respiration. For the lungfish, respiration in the swamp water is no problem because it has true lungs—two sacs opening into the gullet—and comes to the surface to breathe the air. As the swamp waters dry up, the lungfish goes into estivation, a state like hibernation in which all bodily processes are slowed down: the animal keeps alive, caked in the dried mud, until favorable conditions return.

Among the little mosquito-eating cyprinodonts, South America has one egg-laying family and three families which bear their young alive. Most interesting of the egg layers are a number of annual species which normally live less than a year. Some of them grow only an inch or two long, others up to six or eight inches. Nearly all belong to the genus *Cynolebias*. They are partial to swampy ditches and temporary ponds, which often fail to last out the drier months. As the water disappears, the fishes spawn in the mud and then die. In the dry season, the species exists solely in the form of eggs buried in the mud, usually below a hard top crust. When the rains come, this softens up, and the eggs hatch rapidly, often in less than an hour. The young fishes grow fast on microorganisms and mosquito larvae, and within a month a new crop of adult fishes may be present.

Two of the three families of live-bearing cyprinodonts in South America are also worth attention. The family Poeciliidae has the most numerous species, of which the tiny guppy *Poecilia reticulata*, which is native to the lowlands of Guiana, Venezuela and the island of Trinidad, is by far the best known. As a destroyer of mosquito larvae, it has been introduced into other parts of South America, Malaya, India and many other tropical places, where it does as good a job as its relative, *Gambusia*, the North American mosquito fish, and with less destruction of the young of valuable food fishes. Other members of the same family are common in Colombia, western Ecuador and the lands east of the Andes south to the Plata estuary.

The other live-bearing family has one of the strangest of all the world's fishes, the "four-eyed" *Anableps*, which lives in tidal fresh waters from the

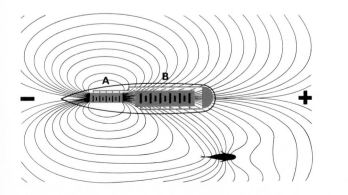
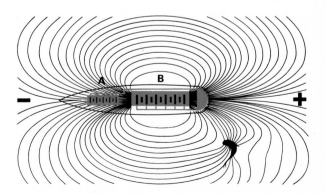

Orinoco delta to the sand coasts near the bulge of Brazil. Here along this muddy mangrove coast one often sees peculiar sets of little V-shaped intersecting ripples, like the wakes of tiny boats, moving along the surface. This is the mark of the four-eyed fish, whose eyes project above its head like those of a pond frog—but with this difference: each eye is divided horizontally, the upper part for vision in the air, the lower for vision in the water. Every few seconds the fish ducks its head, to keep the upper half of the eyes wet. Frighten an *Anableps* and it dives a foot or two; but it has to fight to keep down, and when it is no longer frightened, it bobs right up to the top again, for its air bladder is just big enough to keep it floating with eyes awash.

The great complex water system of the Amazon and the Orinoco also has a number of inhabitants that have moved in from the oceans. Sharks come prowling into the lower reaches of most tropical rivers; in the larger ones they are sometimes found hundreds of miles inland, as are their cousins the giant sawfishes. Sharks and sawfishes are different from true bony fishes in that their skeletons are cartilaginous. This places them in a special class of their own, along with the rays. Almost all of the members of this group are salt-water creatures, and thus it is particularly interesting that one entire group of stingrays, the family Potamotrygonidae, with three genera and numerous species, has adapted itself completely to the fresh waters of the Amazon-Orinoco system. These rays occur everywhere through the rivers, right up to the rushing torrents at the base of the Andes. Like their marine relatives, they have the habit of lying partially buried, and if stepped on, they can inflict a painful wound with the barbed, venom-covered spine halfway down their tails.

Certainly the longest, if not the heaviest, fishes in the Amazon and other big tropical rivers are the salt-water sawfishes (*Pristis*), some of which are said to grow to 20 feet in length. Technically, they are rays, though they have the look of sharks. Their long, flattened beaks, studded on each side with heavy, shark-like teeth, are occasionally displayed in lower Amazon towns and attest to their presence in these waters, although little is known about their habits there.

Very little is known, either, about sharks in the Amazon, but these creatures are caught not only at Manaus, in the middle Amazon, but also at Iquitos, in Peru, over 2,000 miles upriver from the sea! No ichthyologist has ever examined an Amazonian shark, but a photo of one caught at Iquitos was identified by Professor Myers as almost certainly the bull shark *Carcharinus leucas*. This shark, which grows to about 10 feet in length, is the same one which inhabits Lake Nicaragua in Central America.

O NE of the things not often understood about fishes is the fact that so many species are of small size. Averaging out the adult lengths of all the world's species of fishes would probably produce a length of about six or seven inches. In South America, despite a profusion of large fishes, the average size would be even smaller, possibly five inches. This means that the vast majority of adult fishes must be smaller yet, some only an inch or an inch and a half. For this reason, South America is a happy hunting ground for the collectors of small tropical fishes for home aquarium enthusiasts. Chief among these South American aquarium fishes (outside the guppy, which is bred in captivity and rarely imported) are many species of so-called "tetras"—small characins less than three inches in length. The most brilliant, like the neon tetra, are usually from clear, shaded streams in the forest. Species from muddy or unshaded waters, here and elsewhere, tend to be pale in color. Next to the tetras in popularity are

**VARIATIONS
ON A GUPPY THEME**

From stock as simple-looking as the wild guppy (top), breeders have produced guppies as elaborate as the lyretail, triangle and topsword (bottom three). First among aquarium fishes today, the guppy was named after the naturalist Robert Lechmere Guppy, who collected the British Museum's first specimens in Trinidad in 1866. Through selective breeding, males are now often twice as big as their wild ancestors and far more colorful. In some cases, their tails have become so long they must be cut to facilitate mating.

those species known in the trade as "South American cats." These are little armored catfishes of the small and relatively unimportant South American family Callichthyidae. Most of them have patterns of blackish spots, stripes or blotches on a lighter ground color and belong to the genus *Corydoras*.

Also much in demand are the flying characins, called hatchetfishes by aquariists. There are only nine species known, the largest growing to perhaps four inches. They are the world's only true flying fishes—they actually do fly by buzzing their wings, in contrast to the much larger salt-water flying fishes, which merely glide. They are strange little creatures with thin, deep bodies. The part which looks like the blade of a hatchet (the handle being the thin tail) is formed by an enormous pectoral girdle, much like the breastbone of a bird, which anchors the great sheet of muscle with which the "wings," actually the pectoral fins, are powered. The fishes cruise or float along just under the surface film and, when frightened, dart into the air for leaps of six feet or more a few inches above the surface. They move with such lightninglike speed that few people ever *see* them fly, and no one could tell (without a high-speed movie camera) that they do use the fins rather than merely jump. However, the relatively huge pectoral muscles show it, and specimens have been heard to buzz when trying to leap out of a tin can in which they were being carried. They are nervous little fishes and have been found dead in an aquarium, evidently after having tried a quick flight through the glass cover of the tank. Several species are plain, silvery, open-water fishes. Four minute species inhabit forest brooks and have pretty patterns of dark markings.

THE marine fishes of the oceans surrounding South America are in no way as peculiarly characteristic of the continent as the fresh-water ones are. As with marine fishes anywhere, their distribution depends primarily on temperatures, and so it is no surprise to find among them many of the same types of ocean fishes found on North American coasts. However, South America has one strong peculiarity in its marine-fish fauna that is not shared by any other continent. The Antarctic region has many characteristic cold-water, marine shore fishes. The southern tip of South America reaches almost to Antarctic latitudes; as a result, the coastal waters of southern Chile and Patagonia have received a few of the strange cold-water types that otherwise are found only along the ice-edged shores at the very bottom of this world.

Of special note among South American marine fishes are the vast schools of anchovies and sardines in the cold, nutrient-rich waters of the Humboldt Current off the coast of Peru. These fishes form the principal food of the untold millions of sea birds which for more than a century have provided Peru with an extensive fertilizer industry in the form of guano. Nowadays, Peru is building an extensive and important fishery by catching these same sardines and anchovies for human consumption.

Another Peruvian fishery, one which existed for centuries, is today dying out. It is located in one of the most distinctive aquatic environments on this or any other continent: Lake Titicaca, 12,500 feet high in the Andes between Peru and Bolivia. There, along with a species of lake catfish, lives a subfamily of the fresh-water cyprinodonts, which as a group is one of the evolutionary wonders of the fish world. Its 20 species are known as the Orestiinae. Considerably larger than most of their top-minnow relatives elsewhere, they attain a length of as much as 10 inches and were a staple food in this unique, high-altitude region for untold centuries. Unfortunately, lake trout from North America were introduced into Titicaca some 25 years ago, and they throve—some well over 20 pounds have been caught. Much of their growth, however, may have been at the expense of the orestiines, which are now seriously threatened if not already doomed.

Lake Titicaca and its alien trout bring up a fitting subject with which to conclude this book: the unique opportunities which still exist—but not for very much longer—of conserving in South America some of the most distinctive plant and animal species still alive on our planet. We have gone, now, in this survey of Neotropical animals, from monkeys and other mammals to birds, reptiles, amphibians, insects and fishes. We have seen the settings of imposing grandeur in which they live with all their varying opportunities for life—the high Andes, the wind-swept grasslands, the deserts of the Pacific coast, the mighty Amazon with all its allied rivers and streams, and, towering over these, the tremendous forest that covers the heart of the continent. These many habitats have allowed a very great number of species to evolve, from those originating in the long period of South America's isolation to the newcomers from the north which migrated across the land bridge a few million years ago. We have learned how these faunas eliminated each other, competed or blended with each other and with those many other animal groups that came down from ancestors who island-hopped their way along the archipelagoes which formed steppingstones in the seas surrounding the continent.

WHAT is the future of this rich, varied and distinctive fauna? In South America, as elsewhere in the world, this depends primarily on the behavior of the human species. So far, the Neotropical fauna is probably less threatened than that of any other region, because the human population, especially in the rain-forest area, is still relatively sparse. But this same factor has also made the practice of conservation peculiarly difficult, because intelligent conservation requires well-trained people, not just on one level but on many.

For about the first half of the last hundred years, the cause of conservation was promoted mainly by isolated individuals and the scientific community in Latin America. In the late 1920s, governments began to come into the picture, and then, in many cases, the efforts undertaken to create parks and reserves were as unrealistic as they were well intentioned. A good many tracts of land were set aside by various countries, but the conditions governing their use and maintenance were often loosely set forth, leaving loopholes for agriculture and forest industries to exploit them. In most cases, too, the programs outlined far outran the ability of the government to staff them with trained personnel. Finally, simply because South America was—and to a degree still is—a sparsely settled continent, much of its parkland, actual or prospective, was so difficult of access that intelligent and useful administration was almost impossible.

This last factor so far has in large measure acted to protect the wildlife, but very soon it will no longer. With the opening of more and more highways like the Inter-American Highway and its ramifications, the need for real conservation has become a matter of the here and now, not of a comfortably distant future. Now the peoples of the Neotropical region must act—for what can still be done today might well be impossible a generation from now. As E. M. Nicholson, Director General of the English Nature Conservancy, put it on a recent tour of the Pacific-coast areas: "The rate of destruction of habitat can now be measured in acres per hour." A wonderful wilderness is disappearing, and this is a concern not only of Latin Americans but of mankind.

IN A LONG DUGOUT CANOE, CARAJA INDIANS MOVE OVER THE ARAGUAIA RIVER. THE TRIBE HAS RULED HERE SINCE BEFORE COLUMBUS' TIME

A World Wide and Wet

Water—endless miles of river, months of pelting tropical rain—controls life over half of South America. Fishes abound; mammals must adapt to the all-pervading wet or die. Not only tapirs and ant-eaters but even the water-loathing sloth must occasionally swim. To man, the waters give food, roadways out of his jungle clearings and, in flood, cruel blows that can wash away his village overnight.

FISHES TO STOCK HOME AQUARIUMS HAVE BECOME AN IMPORTANT EXPORT OF CENTRAL AND SOUTH AMERICA. THE BURST OF COLOR ABOVE W

The Charms of Little Fishes

The rivers of South and Central America teem with small, beguiling, multihued fishes. Male swordtails, for example, are marvelous jumpers, and chocolate cichlids can blush a rosy pink. Many of the fishes are difficult to breed outside their native waters—often the exact location where they were caught is unknown, and thus conditions there cannot be recreated—but most can live happily in tanks on diets of dried shrimp eggs, mosquito larvae and freshly swatted houseflies. The algae eaters flourish on spinach. And the rule that big fish eat little fish can be circumvented by keeping them all reasonably full.

COLLECTED MOSTLY FROM THE ORINOCO AND AMAZON BASINS. ONE IS THE DISCUS (7, BELOW) THAT FEEDS ITS YOUNG ON ITS OWN SKIN SECRETIONS

The fishes above are identified in the drawing at right. Their cost in New York ranges from three for one dollar (for the neon tetras, which 30 years ago cost $100 each) to $700 for a pair of breeding discuses. From left, top to bottom, the fishes are: (1) serpa tetra; (2) *Moenkhausia;* (3) black tetra; (4) swordtail; (5) eartheater; (6) hatchetfish; (7) discus; (8) silver dollar; (9) leopard corydoras; (10) swordtail characin; (11) spotted headstander; (12) chocolate cichlid; (13) emperor tetra; (14) cardinal tetra; (15) neon tetra; (16) fresh-water angelfish; (17) pretty tetra; (18) gold tetra; (19) lemon tetra; (20) glowlight tetra; (21) rosy tetra; (22) silver-tipped tetra; (23) striped *Anostomus;* (24) dwarf pencilfish; (25) Buenos Aires tetra.

THE AWKWARD SLOTH, called the Nimble Peter by derisive Spaniards, never leaves the trees unless it absolutely has to. But when forced out by floods, it floats and flaps its way along.

In fact it is almost impossible to drown a sloth. Totally immersed for 30 minutes, they will still revive—possibly because their slow metabolism rate requires less oxygen in their blood.

When the Floods Come

The Amazon in flood, moving at a majestic five miles an hour, cuts mazes of new channels and creates thousands of square miles of swamp. Islands of matted vegetation, mangrove and twisted vine as much as two miles wide are torn loose and sent sailing inexorably down the slow sluiceway that every second pours nearly 64 billion gallons of water into the sea. Even before the rains come, the populations of some insects decrease as if in anticipation. Then one day black ants march urgently over the forest floor in long leathery columns; soon the centipedes, lizards, snakes and jaguars join in the flight. But inevitably the waters catch up and everything that can climb a tree does so—as so many forms of terrestrial life have long since learned to do in this land that in the rainy seasons of each year is a virtual inland sea.

A PAIR OF TAPIRS lolls submerged with their curving heads and noses showing. The pony-sized tapirs love water and feed as readily on water organisms as they do on fruit and twigs.

A FAST-SWIMMING GIANT ANTEATER cleaves the water in search of land. Although this species favors high ground and is seldom caught in floods, it can use powerful forepaws in emergencies to achieve a good turn of swimming speed. Other anteaters, living in the rain forest, have learned to live in the trees, where they find food in tree-adapted ants and termites.

THE FRESH-WATER MANATEE, a denizen of the upper Amazon, is a lazy, amiable water mammal easily approached in a dug-out canoe. Like its coastal cousin, it feeds on underwater grasses, suckles its young and rises to make doleful sighing noises as if pleading to be milked. It has been caught 1,000 miles up river and probably ranges at least 1,000 miles more.

FRESH-WATER DOLPHINS, descendants of a family of toothed whales that now live in large river systems, have been clocked at two miles an hour on long swims and as high as 10 in short bursts. They swim near the surface in groups and are fond of making long, graceful leaps as high as four feet out of water. As they age, their dark gray color lightens nearly to white.

A COASTAL MANATEE STICKS ITS BOVINE SNOUT OUT OF WATER TO BREATHE. SAILORS CALL IT THE SE

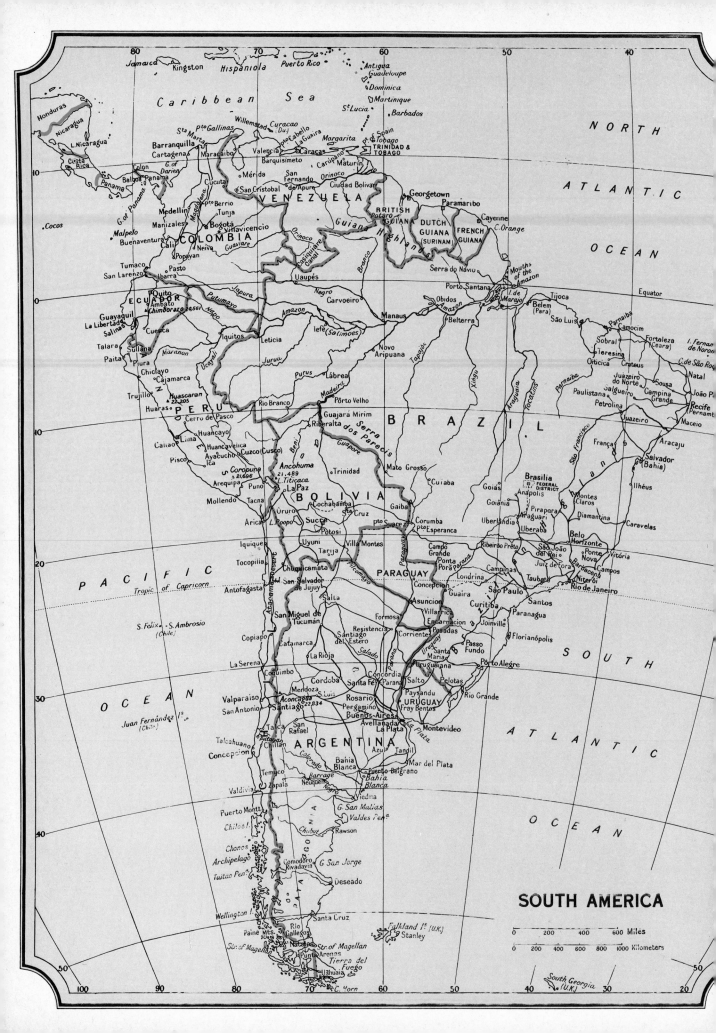

SOUTH AMERICA

Bibliography

Geography and Regional Descriptions

Aübert de la Rue, Edgar, François Bourlière and Jean-Paul Harroy, *The Tropics*. Alfred A. Knopf, 1957.

Bowman, Isaiah, *The Andes of Southern Peru*. American Geographical Society, 1916.

Butland, Gilbert J., *Latin America, a Regional Geography*. Longmans, Green, London, 1960.

Haskins, Caryl P., *The Amazon, the Life History of a Mighty River*. Doubleday, Doran, 1943.

James, Preston E., *Latin America* (3rd ed.). Odyssey Press, 1959.

Kendrew, Wilfrid G., *The Climates of the Continents* (5th ed.). Clarendon Press, 1961.

Richards, P. W., *The Tropical Rain Forest*. Cambridge University Press, 1957.

Schulthess, Emil, *The Amazon*. Simon and Schuster, 1962.

The Naturalists in South America

*Bates, Henry Walter, *The Naturalist on the River Amazon*. Peter Smith, 1963.

Bates, Nancy Bell, *East of the Andes and West of Nowhere*. Charles Scribner's Sons, 1947.

Beebe, Charles William, *High Jungle*. Duell, Sloan & Pearce, 1949.

Carr, Archie, *High Jungles and Low*. University of Florida Press, 1953.

Chapman, Frank M., *Life in an Air Castle*. Appleton-Century, 1938.

Cutright, Paul Russell, *The Great Naturalists Explore South America*. Macmillan, 1940.

Darwin, Charles, *Journal of Researches into the Geology and Natural History of the Various Countries Visited by H.M.S. Beagle*. Hafner, 1952. * Also available under the title of *The Voyage of the Beagle*.

Durrell, Gerald M., *Three Tickets to Adventure*. Viking Press, 1954.

Guenther, Konrad, *A Naturalist in Brazil*. Houghton Mifflin, 1931.

Hingston, R.W.G., *A Naturalist in the Guiana Forest*. Longmans, 1932.

† MacCreagh, Gordon, *White Waters and Black*. Doubleday, 1961.

Miller, Leo E., *In the Wilds of South America*. Scribner, 1918.

Roosevelt, T. R., *Through the Brazilian Wilderness*. Scribner, 1914.

Invertebrate Animals

Buchsbaum, Ralph, and others, *The Lower Animals*. Doubleday, 1960.

Imms, A. D., *Insect Natural History*. Collins, 1947.

Klots, Alexander B., *Living Insects of the World*. Doubleday, 1959.

Pesson, Paul, *The World of Insects*. McGraw-Hill, 1958.

Williams, C. B., *The Migration of Butterflies*. Oliver and Boyd, 1930.

Mammals

*Allen, Glover Merrill, *Bats*. Harvard University Press, 1939.

Bourlière, François, *The Natural History of Mammals*. Alfred A. Knopf, 1964 (revised ed.).

Cabrera, Angel, *Catalogo de los Mamiferos de America del Sur*. Revista del Museo Argentino de Ciencias Naturales "Bernardino Rivadavia" e Instituto Nacional de Investigación de Las Ciencias Naturales (Vol. IV, Nos. 1 & 2), 1957, 1960.

Cabrera, Angel, and José Yepes, *Mamiferos Sud-Americanos*, (2 vols., 2nd ed.) Ediar S. A. Editores, 1960.

Carpenter, C. R., *A Field Study of the Behavior and Social Relations of Howling Monkeys*. Comparative Psychological Monographs (Vol. 10, No. 2), 1934.

Enders, Robert K., *Mammalian Life Histories from Barro Colorado Island, Panama*. Bulletin of the Museum of Comparative Zoology (Vol. 78, No. 4), 1935.

Goodwin, George G., and Arthur M. Greenhall, *A Review of the Bats of Trinidad and Tobago*. Bulletin of the American Museum of Natural History (Vol. 122), 1961.

Griffin, Donald R., *Listening in the Dark*. Yale University Press, 1958.

Hall, E. R., and K. R. Kelson, *The Mammals of North America* (2 vols.). Ronald Press, 1959.

Hershkovitz, Philip, *Mammals of Northern Colombia, Preliminary Report No. 7: Tapirs*. Proceedings of the United States National Museum (Vol. 103), 1956.

Hill, W. C. Osman, *Primates: Comparative Anatomy and Taxonomy* (Vol. 3, 1957; Vol. 4, 1960; Vol. 5, 1962). Interscience Publishers.

Hooton, Earnest, *Man's Poor Relations*. Doubleday, 1942.

*Klüver, Heinrich, *Behavior Mechanisms in Monkeys*. University of Chicago Press, 1933.

Lima, Eladio da Cruz, *Mammals of Amazonia* (Vol. I). Museo Paranese Emilio Goeldi de Historia Natural e Ethnografia, 1945.

Scott, William B., *A History of Land Mammals in the Western Hemisphere* (rev. ed.). Hafner, 1962.

Simpson, George Gaylord, *The Development of Marsupials in South America*. Physis (Vol. XIV), 1939. *The Principles of Classification and a Classification of Mammals*. Bulletin of the American Museum of Natural History (Vol. 85), 1945.

Birds

Allen, Robert Porter, *Birds of the Caribbean*. Viking Press, 1961.

Austin, Oliver L., Jr., *Birds of the World*. Golden Press, 1961.

Chapman, Frank M., *Distribution of Birdlife in Colombia*. Bulletin of the American Museum of Natural History (Vol. 36), 1917. *Distribution of Birdlife in Ecuador*. Bulletin of the American Museum of Natural History (Vol. 55), 1926.

Gilliard, E. Thomas, *Living Birds of the World*. Doubleday, 1958.

Goodall, J. D., A. W. Johnson and R. A. Phillippi B., *Las Aves de Chile* (2 vols.). Platt Establacimentos Graficos, 1957.

Greenewalt, Crawford H., *Hummingbirds*. Doubleday, 1960.

Grossman, Mary Louise, and John N. Hamlet, *Birds of Prey of the World*. Clarkson N. Potter, 1964.

Murphy, Robert Cushman, *Oceanic Birds of South America* (2 vols.). Macmillan, 1948.

Olrog, C. C., *Las Aves Argentinas*. Instituto Miguel Lillo, Universidad de Tucumán, 1955.

Skutch, Alexander F., *Life Histories of Central American Birds*. Cooper Ornithological Society, 1954.

Slud, Paul, *The Birds of Finca "La Selva," Costa Rica: A Tropical Wet Forest Locality*. Bulletin of the American Museum of Natural History (Vol. 121), 1960.

van Tyne, Josselyn, and Andrew J. Berger, *Fundamentals of Ornithology*. John Wiley & Sons, 1961.

Fishes, Amphibians and Reptiles

Cochran, Doris M., *Living Amphibians of the World*. Doubleday, 1961.

Eigenmann, Carl H., and William Ray Allen, *Fishes of Western South America* (Vols. I & II). University of Kentucky, 1942.

Goin, Coleman J. and Olive B., *Introduction to Herpetology*. W. H. Freeman, 1962.

Innes, William T., *Exotic Aquarium Fishes* (ed. by George S. Myers, 19th ed.). Innes, 1956.

Mertens, Robert, *The World of Amphibians and Reptiles*. McGraw-Hill, 1960.

Norman, John Roxburough, and P. H. Greenwood, *A History of Fishes*. Hill and Wang, 1963.

*Oliver, James A., *Snakes in Fact and Fiction*. Macmillan, 1963.

Parker, H. W., *Snakes*. W. W. Norton, 1963.

Schmidt, Karl P., and Robert F. Inger, *Living Reptiles of the World*. Doubleday, 1957.

Sterba, Günther, *Freshwater Fishes of the World*. Viking Press, 1962.

Miscellaneous

Bates, Marston, *Animal Worlds*. Random House, 1963. *The Forest and the Sea*. Random House, 1960. *Where Winter Never Comes*. Charles Scribner's Sons, 1952.

Carr, Archie, *The Windward Road*. Alfred A. Knopf, 1956.

Cott, Hugh B., *Adaptive Coloration in Animals*. Methuen, 1940.

Darlington, Philip J., Jr., *Zoogeography*. John Wiley & Sons, 1957.

Goodspeed, T. Harper, *Plant Hunters in the Andes*. University of California Press, 1961.

Lawrence, George H. M., *Taxonomy of Vascular Plants*. Macmillan, 1951.

Leopold, A. Starker, *Wildlife of Mexico*. University of California Press, 1959.

Polunin, Nicholas, *Introduction to Plant Geography and Some Related Sciences*. McGraw-Hill, 1960.

Simpson, George Gaylord, "History of the Fauna of Latin America," *Science in Progress* (George A. Baitsell, ed.). Yale University Press, 1951 (7th series).

Steward, Julian Haynes, ed., *Handbook of South American Indians* (Vol. III). U.S. Government Printing Office, 1948.

* Also available in paperback edition

† Only available in paperback edition

Credits

The sources for the illustrations in this book are shown below.

Credits for pictures from left to right are separated by commas, top to bottom by dashes.

Cover—Carl W. Rettenmeyer
8—Eliot Elisofon
10, 11—Matt Greene
12—Barbara Wolff
14—Mark Binn
17—A. Y. Owen
18, 19—Map by Matt Greene
20—Antonio Halik
21—A. Y. Owen
22, 23—Douglas Faulkner—
A. Y. Owen
24—Douglas Faulkner
25—Heinz Felten—Anthony
Linck
26, 27—Dmitri Kessel
28, 29—Dmitri Kessel, A. Y.
Owen—Professor Harriet G.
Barclay
30, 31—Emil Schulthess from
Black Star, Thomas
Soderstrom
32—Nina Leen
35—Margaret L. Estey
36—Otto van Eersel
37, 38—Rudolf Freund
41—Harald Schultz
42, 43—Walter Ferguson
44, 45—Shelly Grossman
46—R. S. Simon from Photo Researchers Inc.
47—Federico Medem
48, 49—Shelly Grossman
50—John Hoke
53—Rudolf Freund
55—Rudolf Freund
57—Rudolf Freund
59—Myron Davis
60, 61—J. H. Matternes
62—Courtesy Chicago Natural
History Museum—J. H.
Matternes
63, 64, 65—J. H. Matternes
66, 67—Professor Grzimek;

Frankfurt am Main, Carl W.
Rettenmeyer
68, 69—Carl W. Rettenmeyer
70—Carl W. Rettenmeyer—Car-
los Saravia
71—Courtesy The American Museum of Natural History
72, 73—Allen C. Enders, Karl
Maslowski—Courtesy The
American Museum of Natural
History, New York Zoological
Society Photo
74—Eugen Schuhmacher—Raul
Gonzales—Yale Joel, Pictorial
Parade Inc.
75—Kurt Severin from Black
Star
76—Francis Miller
82, 83—Rudolf Freund
85—Chet Reneson
87—Douglas Faulkner
88, 89—Carl W. Rettenmeyer,
Sasha Seimel—Paulo Muniz
90, 91—Rudolf Freund
92—C. B. Koford
93—Joseph Cellini
94—A. Y. Owen
95—Wendy Hilty from Monk-
meyer Press Photos—Emil
Schulthess from Black Star
96—Shelly Grossman
97—Leonard Lee Rue from An-
nan Photo Features
98—Lilo Hess
100 through 107—Guy Tudor
109—Paul Schwartz
110—Harald Schultz
111—Paul Schwartz from Photo
Researchers Inc. except right
Harald Schultz
112, 113—Paris-Match—Photo
Researchers Inc.
114, 115—New York Zoological

Society Photo except center
Crawford H. Greenewalt © The
American Museum of Natural
History
116, 117—Crawford H. Greenewalt © The American Museum
of Natural History
118, 119—Ed Keffel from "O
Cruzeiro," Crawford H. Greenewalt © The American Museum
of Natural History
120—Lee Boltin
121—E. A. Gourley—Hart
Preston
122, 123—M. Woodbridge
Williams
124—Herb Snitzer
126—René Martin
127—Mark Binn
130, 131—René Martin
133, 134—René Martin
135—New York Zoological Society Photo
136—Jocelyn Crane for New York
Zoological Society courtesy
Duell, Sloan & Pearce, Inc.
137—Janis Roze
138, 139—James L. Vial, Richard
G. Zweifel—David B. Wake,
Edward S. Ross
140, 141—R. S. Simmons except
bottom left Harald Schultz,
Richard G. Zweifel
142—Carl W. Rettenmeyer
143—top Janis Roze—Russ
Kinne from Photo Researchers
Inc.—Bucky Reeves from National Audubon Society
144—John Hoke
145, 146, 147—Birnback Publish-
ing Service
148—Othmar Danesch
151—Margaret L. Estey

153 through 155—Margaret L.
Estey
159—Fritz Goro
160—Dr. Thomas Eisner
161—M. Woodbridge Williams
162—Carl W. Rettenmeyer—
Edward S. Ross
163—Edward S. Ross except bot
tom right Alfred Eisenstaedt
164, 165—Dr. Alexander B. Klot
Edward S. Ross, Carl W. Rettenmeyer, Edward S. Ross—
Edward S. Ross, Carl W. Rett
meyer, Carl W. Rettenmeyer—
Carl W. Rettenmeyer, Edward
S. Ross, Edward S. Ross
166, 167—Karl Weidman from
National Audubon Society
168, 169—Eric Schaal
170—Carl W. Rettenmeyer
171—Lee Boltin
172, 173—Jocelyn Crane from
New York Zoological Society
174, 175—Edward S. Ross
176, 177—Emil Schulthess from
Black Star
178, 179—Margaret L. Estey
180, 181—Stephen Chan
182, 183—Drawings by Gaetano
Di Palma
187—Emil Schulthess from Blac
Star
188, 189—Douglas Faulkner—
Mark Binn
190—John Hoke
191—Carl Gans—Harald Schult
192—Harald Schultz—James N.
Layne Department of Conservation; Cornell University
193—Robert W. Kelley
194—Map by John Bartholomev
Ltd.
Back Cover—Matt Greene

Acknowledgments

The editors of this book are particularly indebted to Richard G. Van Gelder, Chairman and Associate Curator, Department of Mammalogy, The American Museum of Natural History, who read the text in its entirety. Other associates of The American Museum of Natural History who helped with the book are: Dean Amadon, Chairman and Lamont Curator of Birds, Department of Ornithology; James W. Atz, Associate Curator, Department of Ichthyology; Junius B. Bird, Curator of South American Archeology, Department of Anthropology; Charles M. Bogert, Chairman and Curator, Department of Herpetology; Eugene Eisenmann, Research Associate, Department of Ornithology; Willis J. Gertsch, Curator, Department of Entomology; Crawford H. Greenewalt, Research Associate, Department of Ornithology; Malcolm C. McKenna, Assistant Curator, Department of Vertebrate Paleontology; Nicholas S. Obraztsov, Research Fellow, Department of Entomology; Janis Roze, Research Associate, Richard G. Zweifel, Curator, Department of Herpetology; the library staff.

The editors also want to thank Donald Baird, Assistant Curator of Vertebrate Paleontology, Princeton University; François Bourlière, Professor, Faculté de Médecine de Paris; Maria Buchinger, Executive Secretary, Latin American Committee of National Parks; George W. Carey, Department of Social Studies, Teachers College, Columbia University; C. R. Carpenter, Professor of Psychology, Pennsylvania State University; Gates Clark, United States National Museum; John Cohen; Joseph A. Davis, Jr., Curator of Mammals, New York Zoological Park; Paul Diament, Department of Electrical Engineering, Columbia University; Thomas Eisner, Assistant Professor of Entomology, Cornell University; Allen Enders, Associate Professor of Anatomy, Washington University School of Medicine; G. E. Erikson, Assistant

Professor of Anatomy, Harvard Medical School; Richard Etheridge, Assistant Professor of Zoology, San Diego State College; Lee Finneran, Curator-Director, New England Aquarium; Henry Fleming, Research Associate, New York Botanical Garden; Carl Gans, Professor of Biology, New York State University at Buffalo; Harold Grant, Curator, Department of Entomology, Academy of Natural Sciences of Philadelphia; Charles O. Handley, Jr., United States National Museum; William Hart, International Commission on National Parks; Philip Hershkovitz, Research Curator, Chicago Natural History Museum; John Hoke, Atlantic Research Corporation; Glen Jepsen, Sinclair Professor of Vertebrate Paleontology, Princeton University; John H. Kaufmann, Assistant Professor of Biology, University of Florida; Richard M. Klein, Curator of Plant Physiology, New York Botanical Garden; Alexander B. Klots, Professor of Biology, The City College of New York; Heinrich Klüver, Department of Biological Psychology, University of Chicago; Federico Medem, National University, Bogotá; George Myers, Professor of Biology, Stanford University; Rosendo Pascual, University of La Plata, Argentina; Bryan Patterson, Museum of Comparative Zoology, Harvard University; Randolph L. Peterson, Curator of Mammalogy, Royal Ontario Museum of Zoology, Toronto; Fernando Dias de Avila-Pires, Curator of Mammals, Museu Nacional, Rio de Janeiro; Carl W. Rettenmeyer, Assistant Professor of Entomology, School of Agriculture, Kansas State University; Alfred S. Romer, Alexander Agassiz Professor of Zoology, Harvard University; Edward S. Ross, Department of Entomology, California Academy of Sciences, San Francisco; R. Meyer de Schauensee, Chairman and Curator of Birds, Academy of Natural Sciences of Philadelphia; Charles Walker, Curator of Herpetology, Museum of Zoology, University of Michigan.

Index

PRINTED IN U.S.A.
✕✕✕✕✕